On Writers
& Writing

By Helen Sheehy and Leslie Stainton

Published by Tide-mark Press Ltd.

 New Moon First Quarter ○ Full Moon ◑ Last Quarter

Design and Typography by Corry Kaeser Cote

Going to Him! Happy letter!
Tell Him—
Tell Him the page I did'nt write—
Tell Him—I only said the Syntax—
And left the Verb and the pronoun out—
Tell Him just how the fingers hurried—
Then—how they waded—slow—slow—
And then you wished you had eyes in your pages—
So you could see what moved them so—

Tell Him—it was'nt a Practised Writer—
You guessed—from the way the sentence toiled—
You could hear the Boddice tug, behind you—
As if it held but the might of a child—
You almost pitied it—you—it worked so—
Tell Him —no—you may quibble there—
For it would split His Heart, to know it—
And then you and I, were silenter.

Tell Him—Night finished—before we finished—
And the Old Clock kept neighing "Day"!
And you—got sleepy —and begged to be ended—
What could it hinder so—to say?
Tell Him—just how she sealed you—Cautious!
But—if He ask where you are hid
Until tomorrow—Happy letter!
Gesture Coquette—and shake your head!

—Emily Dickinson, Version I, 1862

The Art of the Letter

"I sometimes start the day with the letters," poet May Sarton said. "Just to get the oil into the machine."

Erskine Caldwell likewise recommended letter writing as a means to an end. When you've got writer's block, Caldwell advised, "You can always write something. . . . You write a love letter. You do something to get you in the habit of writing again."

John Steinbeck urged writers paralyzed by the prospect of publication to compose their work "as a letter aimed at one person. This removes the vague terror of addressing the large and faceless audience." Decades earlier Emily Dickinson voiced the same idea when she christened her poetry "my letter to the world, / That never wrote to me."

Letter writing has long been part and parcel of the writer's life. Virginia Woolf drafted thousands of letters in her career, of which some 3,800 survive. "A true letter," she said, "should be a film of wax pressed close to the graving in the mind." Letters were for Woolf a means of sustaining friendships while basking in the solitude she required. They were also a way of recording her observations of the world—observations she later distilled into novelistic prose.

To poet Federico García Lorca, a letter was a precious gift destined for a cherished friend; often Lorca embellished his correspondence with whimsical drawings. In letters, he articulated his evolving aesthetic vision, much as George Sand and Gustave Flaubert did in their decade-long correspondence with one another. Author Francine du Plessix Gray has characterized the exchange of letters between these two French writers as a long epistolary "dialogue on life versus art."

The art of the letter gave rise in the eigthteenth century to the epistolary novel, which survives in our own time in works like Alice Walker's *The Color Purple*, Michael Frayn's *The Trick of It*, and even Andrew Davies's short story *Dirty Faxes*. Samuel Richardson, however, remains the form's greatest practitioner. When his *Pamela* appeared in 1741, readers were so enthralled by the epistolary tale that many believed it to be an actual correspondence of which Richardson was merely the editor.

Letters today seem a vestige of a bygone age. Philip Larkin longingly recounts a world in which letters, "greedily received and faithfully dispatched," were "relied on to combat the ills of daily existence." There is a kind of magic to the letter that no telephone call can match. As Auden reminds us, "To 'long for certain letters' is to be fully human, and to admit a common humanity."

Sunday
31

Monday
1

Tuesday
2

Wednesday
3

Thursday
4

○ Friday
5

Saturday
6
Carl Sandburg, b. 1878

December 1995					
S	M	T	W	T	F	S
					1	2
3	4	5	6	7	8	9
10	11	12	13	14	15	16
17	18	19	20	21	22	23
24	25	26	27	28	29	30
31						

January
1996

February						
S	M	T	W	T	F	S
				1	2	3
4	5	6	7	8	9	10
11	12	13	14	15	16	17
18	19	20	21	22	23	24
25	26	27	28	29		

Sunday
7
Zora Neale Hurston, b. 1891

Monday
8

Wilkie Collins, b. 1824

Tuesday
9

Wednesday
10

Thursday
11

Jack London, b. 1876

Friday
12

Saturday ◐
13

December 1995						
S	M	T	W	T	F	S
					1	2
3	4	5	6	7	8	9
10	11	12	13	14	15	16
17	18	19	20	21	22	23
24	25	26	27	28	29	30
31						

January
1996

February						
S	M	T	W	T	F	S
				1	2	3
4	5	6	7	8	9	10
11	12	13	14	15	16	17
18	19	20	21	22	23	24
25	26	27	28	29		

At the height of his writing career, William Wilkie Collins earned an estimated £10,000 in one year—the highest reported annual income of any nineteenth-century writer. A burly, bearded Victorian, he cultivated a taste for fine food, champagne, crimson ties and blue-striped shirts. Of his penchant for French cuisine he remarked to a friend, "My style is expensive. I look on meat simply as a material for sauces."

In retrospect, his formula for authorial success was simple. "Make 'em cry, make 'em laugh, make 'em wait." An expert at page-turner plots and riveting scenes, Wilkie Collins was the leading sensation novelist of the Victorian age. The son of a well-known British landscape painter, Collins grew up with an artist's eye and toyed with becoming a painter before he turned to writing. With their meticulously rendered settings, his thirty-odd novels and plays attest to his visual gifts.

Wilkie Collins
(January 8, 1824 — September 23, 1889)

Collins drew his most famous book, *The Woman in White* (1860), from his moonlit encounter one night with a woman in white robes who ran screaming from the gates of a London villa as Collins and a pair of friends happened to be passing by. "I must see who she is, and what is the matter," said Collins, and promptly ran after her. The woman, Caroline Graves, not only inspired Collins' novel—about a wife who is imprisoned in a private asylum by her nefarious husband—but she became his lover as well.

In many ways Collins' life was as sensational as the novels which made him famous. For years he supported two illegitimate households: that of his mistress Martha Rudd and the three children she bore him, and that of Caroline Graves, who lived with Collins after her marriage to a plumber failed. But unlike his good friend Charles Dickens, who earned England's scorn when he left his wife for another woman, Collins maintained respectability by declaring himself a bachelor all his life.

He decried the "clap-trap morality" of his age. In his books he combined accurate depictions of contemporary life with the guile and romance of crime, and he thus paved the way for the modern detective novel. As an admiring Henry James once observed, Collins "introduced into fiction those most mysterious of mysteries, the mysteries which are at our own doors."

Don Pedro Calderón de la Barca
(January 17, 1600 — May 25, 1681)

In his most famous work he asked, "What is life?" Life, he answered, "is a dream, / and dreams are dreams." And then, as though to torment himself, he asked if it was not a dream to say that life is a dream.

The mind of Don Pedro Calderón de la Barca thrived on this sort of conundrum. He was better educated and far more erudite than his Golden Age peer, Lope de Vega, the prolific Spanish playwright with whom Calderón is most often compared. He was also more exacting, drafting a mere 110 or so plays in his lifetime as opposed to the 1,500 Lope is reputed to have written.

Their careers overlapped by only a few years. But Lope lived long enough to acknowledge his compatriot's talent. When Calderón won third prize in a poetry competition at the age of twenty-two, the sixty-year old Lope praised him publicly, noting that "at such a tender age [he] has earned laurels which time generally bestows only upon those with white hair." Thirteen years later Lope died, and Calderón succeeded him as the official court playwright to Philip IV.

To Lope's formula for riveting drama Calderón added sumptuous images and a profusion of rhetorical figures, as well as the intellectual residue of his long years of study in Spain's finest schools and universities. While some have criticized his work as "cold" and "mathematical," others extol it. Goethe said of Calderón's plays, they represent the "quintessence of humanity." Fellow Spaniard Federico García Lorca hailed him as the father of modern lyric poetry. Lorca titled one of his own last plays *The Dream of Life*, because, he said, Calderón had already seized the perfect title, *Life Is A Dream*.

In a sense Calderón's life was its own dream. Shielded from the poverty and turmoil of his age by an aristocratic upbringing and a court career, he devoted himself to the creation of fictions for royal audiences. Towards the end of his life, not long after his mistress's death, he became a priest. He spent his last decades writing *autos sacramentales* for public performance during Corpus Christi.

On Pentecost Sunday, 1681, while at work on an *auto sacramental*, Calderón died, "almost singing, like a swan." Some 3,000 admirers attended his funeral. At his own request, Calderón was buried in an open coffin, so that the public could behold the transitory nature of life as it gazed upon his decaying face.

Sunday
14
Yukio Mishima, b. 1925

Monday
15

Molière, b. 1622
Martin Luther King, Jr. Day, born 1929

Tuesday
16

Wednesday
17

Anne Brontë, b. 1820
Don Pedro Calderón de la Barca

Thursday
18

A. A. Milne, b. 1882

Friday
19

Edgar Allan Poe, b. 1809

 ### Saturday
20
Richard Le Gallienne, b. 1866

December 1995						
S	M	T	W	T	F	S
					1	2
3	4	5	6	7	8	9
10	11	12	13	14	15	16
17	18	19	20	21	22	23
24	25	26	27	28	29	30
31						

January
1996

February						
S	M	T	W	T	F	S
				1	2	3
4	5	6	7	8	9	10
11	12	13	14	15	16	17
18	19	20	21	22	23	24
25	26	27	28	29		

Sunday
21

Monday
22

George Gordon, Lord Byron, b. 1788

Tuesday
23

Wednesday
24

Thursday
25

Virgina Woolf, b. 1882

Friday
26

Saturday ◐
27
Lewis Carroll, b. 1832

December 1995						
S	M	T	W	T	F	S
					1	2
3	4	5	6	7	8	9
10	11	12	13	14	15	16
17	18	19	20	21	22	23
24	25	26	27	28	29	30
31						

January
1996

February						
S	M	T	W	T	F	S
				1	2	3
4	5	6	7	8	9	10
11	12	13	14	15	16	17
18	19	20	21	22	23	24
25	26	27	28	29		

In the end he renounced his vocation, telling a friend that "he who is only a poet has done little for mankind." With that he set out "to prove in his own person that a poet may be a soldier," and in the summer of 1823, at the age of thirty-five, George Gordon Noel Byron joined the Greek patriots in their War of Independence from the Turks. When he showed up on the Greek mainland wearing a red military uniform, troops hailed him as a "Messiah." The following spring, his body ravaged by months of battle and cold winter rains, Byron fell ill. On Easter Monday, 1824, at age thirty-six, he died.

All along he had sensed that his work would outlive him. "My mind may lose its force, my blood its fire," he wrote in *Childe Harold's Pilgrimage*. ". . . / But there is that within me which shall tire / Torture and Time, and breathe when I expire."

George Gordon, Lord Byron
(January 22, 1788 — April 19, 1824)

In his brief, convulsive existence George Gordon, the sixth Lord Byron of Rochdale, Nottinghamshire, made of his work and life alike a legend to last the ages. His poems—among them *Childe Harold*, an autobiographical account of the poet's European wanderings, and *Don Juan*, his satirical epic about the fabled Spanish lover—inspired artists from Berlioz and Tchaikovsky, to J.M.W. Turner and Eugène Delacroix, to Pushkin and Heine. (Heine also copied Byron's open-necked shirts.)

The most notorious Romantic of his day, Byron commenced his love life while still a boy and from then on enjoyed a constant stream of lovers, including his half-sister, Augusta, with whom he appears to have had a daughter. Nor did he confine his infatuations to women alone. Lady Caroline Lamb judged Byron "mad—bad—and dangerous to know." His one wife, Annabella, left him soon after the birth of their only child because she could not abide his deranged behavior and drunken abuse.

Throughout Byron's tumultuous life, writing consoled him. After one foiled love affair he confided to a friend, "All convulsions end with me in rhyme; and to solace my mid-nights, I have scribbled another Turkish Tale." Even in war he continued to write, drafting a love poem to his fifteen-year old page boy shortly before his death.

In death Byron became a hero of Greece. But to the world today he is revered as a poet. In the end, his greatest achievement was the one he renounced.

Freya Stark
(January 31, 1893 — May 9, 1993)

Virtually scalped on one side of her head when, as a child, she unwittingly caught her hair in a piece of factory machinery, Freya Stark bore deep facial scars throughout her life. She was never pretty, and towards middle age she admitted, "I always find it takes people about a month to overcome their first impressions of my plainness." Nonetheless, this small, sturdy woman dazzled acquaintances with her sparkling blue eyes, bewildering array of hats, and her keen wit. Once, after foiling a burglary, she quipped, "I had a gun, they had not."

Her prose was just as astonishing. In the twenty-four travel books and autobiographies and eight volumes of letters she produced in her lifetime, Freya Stark created a lucid, spontaneous, elegant style that would inspire generations of writers. About landscape she was passionate. "I like these slow yellow streams," she wrote in *Baghdad Sketches*, a tale of her journey to Iraq. "As they silt up or shift in their lazy beds, they remove cities bodily from one district to another. They are as indolent and wayward, powerful, beneficent and unpitying as the Older Gods whom no doubt they represent . . ."

That Freya Stark should have become a great traveler and writer was by no means pre-ordained. She took her first extensive trip, to Lebanon, in 1927, at the age of thirty-four. Before that she lived quietly on a farm with her mother. Lebanon awakened her wander-lust, however, and from then on Stark devoted her life to travel. She explored much of the Middle East, traveling by camel, mule, and vehicle throughout the Islamic world. She lived in harems, Bedouin tents, and once, to her surprise, in the prostitutes' quarter of Baghdad. To friends she explained that she deliberately risked danger so as not to fear death.

Her letters to family and friends, which she wrote on self-duplicating sheets of paper, formed the basis for many of her books. The impulse to communicate, she found, came most easily when she addressed herself to a particular individual.

"What is it that everyone carries through life, individual to him?" Freya Stark once asked, then answered: "The Horizon." It was the one thing she pursued throughout her life. In her late eighties, Stark climbed the Himalayas. At ninety-three she talked of going to Spain. She lived to be over 100. She died at her hill-town home, Asolo, outside of Venice, and is buried there, dressed in Arabian robes, with the Cross of St. John around her neck.

Sunday
28
Sidonie-Gabrielle Colette, b. 1873

Monday
29

Anton Chekhov, b. 1860

Tuesday
30

Wednesday
31

Zane Grey, b. 1872
Freya Stark, b. 1893

Thursday
1

Friday
2

Ayn Rand, b. 1905

Saturday
3
Gertrude Stein, b. 1874

January/February
1996

December 1995						
S	M	T	W	T	F	S
					1	2
3	4	5	6	7	8	9
10	11	12	13	14	15	16
17	18	19	20	21	22	23
24	25	26	27	28	29	30
31						

February						
S	M	T	W	T	F	S
				1	2	3
4	5	6	7	8	9	10
11	12	13	14	15	16	17
18	19	20	21	22	23	24
25	26	27	28	29		

Sunday ○
4

Monday
5

Tuesday
6

Christopher Marlowe, b. 1564

Wednesday
7

Laura Ingalls Wilder, b. 1867

Thursday
8

Kate Chopin, b. 1850

Friday
9

Amy Lowell, b. 1874

Saturday
10
Bertolt Brecht, b. 1898

January						
S	M	T	W	T	F	S
	1	2	3	4	5	6
7	8	9	10	11	12	13
14	15	16	17	18	19	20
21	22	23	24	25	26	27
28	29	30	31			

February
1996

March						
S	M	T	W	T	F	S
					1	2
3	4	5	6	7	8	9
10	11	12	13	14	15	16
17	18	19	20	21	22	23
24	25	26	27	28	29	30
31						

Ezra Pound wickedly called her "our only hippo-poetess."

A large woman with huge ambitions, she was not the most gifted poet in the zoo of modern poetry, but she was poetry's ardent champion.

Amory, the name her parents gave her when she was born, suited her much better than the diminutive Amy with which they christened her. She was the last child in a wealthy Boston family (her brother Abbott Lawrence Lowell was the President of Harvard), and she grew up in a Brookline brownstone mansion that boasted a library of 7,000 books. Tutored by governesses, encouraged early on to write, taken on trips abroad, Amy Lowell reaped all the advantages of privilege and financial security. These gave her the freedom to take a path other than debutante, wife, and mother and

Amy Lowell
(February 9, 1874 — May 12, 1925)

to become a serious poet, a liberated woman, and a celebrated eccentric who smoked cigars, wore mannish suits and a pince-nez, and lived with a woman companion. "I too am a rare Pattern," she wrote in *Patterns*, her most memorable poem.

She was an original, a sort of Amazon of poetry, autocratic, formidable, and armed with a high-minded determination to refine the taste of the American public. Her first book, *A Dome of Many-Coloured Glass*, sold just eighty copies; in later works she experimented with polyphonic verse—a kind of unrhymed cadence. She published her own collections of poetry, edited the poetry of others, wrote a well-received biography of her hero John Keats as well as various critical studies, and traveled America on lecture and reading tours.

She had literary friendships with D. H. Lawrence, Thomas Hardy, and Ezra Pound, and she was an astute observer of other women poets. About her "sisters" she wrote: "Sappho would speak, I think, quite openly, / And Mrs. Browning guard a careful silence, / But Emily would set doors ajar and slam them / And love you for your speed of observation."

Amy Lowell knew that she did not possess the verbal magic of her earlier poet sisters—her own words were "little jars" to "take and put upon a shelf"—but when she died, Robert Frost grieved. "We all lost a publicity agent," he said. "She stomped the country for everyone."

"All books are either dreams or swords," she believed. "You can cut, or you can drug, with words."

Charles Darwin

(February 12, 1809 — April 19, 1882)

"I was born to be a naturalist," said Charles Darwin, who began his formal education at a Shropshire day school when he was eight-and-a-half days old. There he displayed a marked interest in collecting pebbles, stones, newts, birds' eggs and beetles.

But he was no student. At boarding school his teachers viewed him as an "ordinary boy," and his father, angry at his predilection for "dogs and ratcatching," predicted he would be "a disgrace" to himself and his family.

At Cambridge, where he studied briefly for the clergy, Darwin spent most of his time collecting beetles. Such was his zeal that one day, in an attempt to seize three rare beetles at once, he popped one into his mouth. "Alas it ejected some intensely acrid fluid ... so that I was forced to spit the beetle out."

Because of his aptitude for science, he was asked in 1831 to accompany a British brig as it surveyed the South American coast, the South Seas, and the Indian archipelago. The ship was the H.M.S. Beagle. The expedition changed both Darwin's life and the course of human knowledge.

During his long journey Darwin amassed hordes of scientific data. He also learned to write. The Beagle's captain thought parts of Darwin's journal worthy of publication, and in Britain a friend was so smitten by the naturalist's lively letters home that he printed a selection of them.

Darwin spent the next two decades transforming the raw material of his Beagle voyage into the articles and books on which his fame now rests, most significantly *On the Origin of the Species*. With this revolutionary book Darwin defied almost every convention of nineteenth-century belief. "God knows what the public will think," he said on the eve of the work's publication in 1859.

The public welcomed it. The book's first edition sold out in a day. While many critics attacked its heterodoxy, others defended its logic, and still others revelled in its readable style. For in writing his most famous work Darwin employed the techniques of popular literature. His sense of the genre had been honed by years of listening to his wife read romantic novels out loud while he reclined on his sofa at home.

In his final years, Darwin turned his attention to a new book, *The Formation of Vegetable Mould, through the Action of Worms, with Observations on Their Habits*. As he labored on this, his last work, he confessed, "My heart and soul care for worms and nothing else in the world just at present." Born a naturalist, Charles Darwin remained one to the end.

Sunday
11

◑ *Monday*
12

Tuesday
13

Wednesday
14

Thursday
15

Friday
16

Saturday
17

January						
S	M	T	W	T	F	S
	1	2	3	4	5	6
7	8	9	10	11	12	13
14	15	16	17	18	19	20
21	22	23	24	25	26	27
28	29	30	31			

February
1996

March						
S	M	T	W	T	F	S
					1	2
3	4	5	6	7	8	9
10	11	12	13	14	15	16
17	18	19	20	21	22	23
24	25	26	27	28	29	30
31						

Sunday
18
●

Monday
19

Carson McCullers, b. 1917
Presidents' Day
Heritage Day (Canada)

Tuesday
20

Wednesday
21

Ash Wednesday

Thursday
22

Edna St. Vincent Millay, b. 1892
George Washington, born 1732

Friday
23

W.E.B. Du Bois, b. 1868
Samuel Pepys, b. 1633

Saturday
24

January						
S	M	T	W	T	F	S
	1	2	3	4	5	6
7	8	9	10	11	12	13
14	15	16	17	18	19	20
21	22	23	24	25	26	27
28	29	30	31			

February
1996

March						
S	M	T	W	T	F	S
					1	2
3	4	5	6	7	8	9
10	11	12	13	14	15	16
17	18	19	20	21	22	23
24	25	26	27	28	29	30
31						

Samuel Pepys
(February 23, 1633 — May 25, 1703)

When we hear the name Pepys ("peeps"), we think diary. "So to sleep, every day bringing me a fresh sense of the pleasure of my present life," purred Samuel Pepys on April 17, 1660. And, on August 11, 1660, he noted that "I rose today without any pain, which makes me think that my pain yesterday was nothing but from my drinking too much the day before."

He recorded the trifles and the triumphs of his days, rose into the top ranks of the British government (becoming a Member of Parliament and Secretary of the Admiralty), but Samuel Pepys is remembered, usually with a smile, because of his diary written between January 1, 1660, through May 31, 1669.

Deciphered over a century after Pepys' death, the diaries tell us that he loved Elizabeth, his stylish, half-French wife. He quarreled with her about her command of the servants and her wearing of a light colored wig. She reproached him with his drinking and his dalliances with the servant girls. He blackened her eye; she attacked him with red-hot fireplace tongs. They made-up, usually with hours of "sporting" in bed. One evening he drank three quarts of wine, ate two hundred walnuts, and not surprisingly felt ill the next morning. He had a case made to preserve his kidney stone and wore a rabbit's foot to keep off the colic. Stricken with failing eyesight, "this morning I was let blood, and did bleed about fourteen ounces," he records.

His diary begins with the Restoration, and he was on the ship that carried King Charles back to his English throne. An avid theatregoer, he reported and applauded the introduction of actresses onto the English stage (he enjoyed *Macbeth*, but thought *A Midsummer Night's Dream* a "most insipid, ridiculous play"), paid a shilling to watch a thief hanged, worried about the nits in his periwig, and looked at the stars through a telescope. Pepys survived the Great Plague and reported that the grass grew in London streets as the population died or fled the city. During the Great Fire of London, he saw pigeons fly with burning wings, and he suffered terrifying nightmares of fire and collapsing houses.

Sir Walter Scott called Pepys a "curious fellow." Diarist John Evelyn, his friend of forty years, agreed, eulogizing Pepys as a "very worthy, industrious and curious person . . . He was universally beloved."

Pepys simply said that he was "with child to see any strange thing."

Henry Wadsworth Longfellow
(February 27, 1807 — March 24, 1882)

Apollonian in looks as well as stature, Henry Wadsworth Longfellow was the most popular poet of his age. Queen Victoria numbered among his admirers. So did Charles Dickens and Alfred Tennyson, Franz Liszt and Abraham Lincoln. And an unnamed American schoolchild who was asked at church one day to name the single book that all good people loved to read. "Longfellow's *Poems*," she replied.

He relished fine wines and posh attire, European literature and Puritan ideals. A native New Englander who believed that "to stay at home is best," Longfellow wrote *Evangeline*, *The Courtship of Miles Standish*, and *The Song of Hiawatha* from the comfort of his Massachusetts study, without so much as a glimpse of their real-life settings. Books taught him everything he needed to know. He was a scholar of modern languages before he became a poet, and even after he took up poetry he taught for two decades at Harvard University. In 1854 he resigned in order to write fulltime. He was the first American poet to live off his royalties.

But Longfellow's charmed existence came to a harsh end on July 9, 1861. That day his beloved wife of eighteen years, Fanny Appleton Longfellow, came running into his study, her dress in flames. While sealing up locks of her daughters' hair, she had suddenly caught fire from a match or a piece of burning wax. Longfellow tried in vain to extinguish the flames that engulfed her, but he merely burned his face and hands instead. Fanny Longfellow died the following day.

The poet clipped a lock of his wife's hair and slipped it into an envelope on the day of her death, together with a poem which reads, in part, "And when the dark lock I behold, / I wish that I were dead." To his sister-in-law he confided, "How I am alive after what my eyes have seen, I know not. . . . I loved her so entirely." For the remainder of his life he was haunted by her memory.

If Longfellow's verse strikes us today as sentimental, we would do well to remember "the fragility of domestic happiness" in the century that preceded ours, writes poet Dana Gioia in his eloquent appraisal of Longfellow in *The Columbia History of American Poetry*. Longfellow represents "the traditional aesthetic Modernism defined itself against," Gioia argues, and thus his work has been "damned." But his finest poems are a permanent part of our literature. Adds Gioia, "You will have to go a long way round if you want to ignore him."

Sunday
25
Carlo Goldoni, b. 1707

◑ *Monday*
26

Victor Hugo, b. 1802

Tuesday
27

Henry Wadsworth Longfellow, b. 1807
John Steinbeck, b. 1902

Wednesday
28

Michel de Montaigne, b. 1533

Thursday
29

Friday
1

Saturday
2

	January				
S	M	T	W	T	F	S

S	M	T	W	T	F	S
	1	2	3	4	5	6
7	8	9	10	11	12	13
14	15	16	17	18	19	20
21	22	23	24	25	26	27
28	29	30	31			

February/March
1996

March

S	M	T	W	T	F	S
					1	2
3	4	5	6	7	8	9
10	11	12	13	14	15	16
17	18	19	20	21	22	23
24	25	26	27	28	29	30
31						

Sunday
3

Monday
4

Tuesday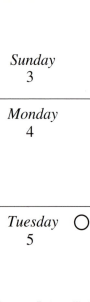
5

Constance Fenimore Woolson, b. 1840

Wednesday
6

Elizabeth Barrett Browning, b. 1806
Ring Lardner, b. 1885

Thursday
7

Friday
8

Saturday
9
Vita Sackville-West, b. 1892

February						
S	M	T	W	T	F	S
				1	2	3
4	5	6	7	8	9	10
11	12	13	14	15	16	17
18	19	20	21	22	23	24
25	26	27	28	29		

March
1996

April						
S	M	T	W	T	F	S
	1	2	3	4	5	6
7	8	9	10	11	12	13
14	15	16	17	18	19	20
21	22	23	24	25	26	27
28	29	30				

In 1845 Henry David Thoreau shut himself away in a cabin in order to contemplate nature and record his contemplations. More than a century later, Annie Dillard took refuge in an uninsulated island cabin on Puget Sound so that she could do the same.

American writers have always had a particular affinity for nature. More so than their European counterparts, whose pastoral accounts of landscape depict a continent subdued by civilization, Americans have from the start tangled with the call of the wild. To the first chroniclers of America, the New World "represented the oldest world, pristine," writes critic Alfred Kazin. "It was the beginning of things, without man to sully the picture."

Even the Declaration of Independence grants authority to "the laws of nature and to Nature's God." The author of that document, Thomas Jefferson, was one of America's first and finest observers

Nature's Nation

of the natural world. His *Notes on the State of Virginia*, culled from Jefferson's exhaustive knowledge of the boundaries, rivers, seaports, mountains, manners and laws of his native state, exudes "the excitement of some fabulous first encounter," writes Kazin. That same "thrill of discovery" would find refrain in the works of Thoreau, Whitman, Melville, Twain, Hemingway, Frost, Dillard and McPhee.

To Emily Dickinson nature provided a language for expressing her deepest intuitions. To Ralph Waldo Emerson it supplied the subject and title of his first book. "I feel," he wrote in his 1836 masterpiece, *Nature*, "that nothing can befall me in life, —no disgrace, no calamity, (leaving me my eyes,) which nature cannot repair."

Henry David Thoreau called himself a "bachelor of nature." Walt Whitman, revelling in his attachment to the natural world, spoke of "Earth, my likeness." John Greenleaf Whittier and Henry Wadsworth Longfellow domesticated nature; Herman Melville recounted its savage power. Ernest Hemingway celebrated its variety, while Robert Frost examined its decay.

Today's poets, novelists and essayists tend to document nature's desecration rather than its charms. "Lord, let me die but not die / out," writes poet James Dickey. The country that once thought of itself as "nature's nation" has given way to a developer's paradise. "In wildness is the preservation of the world," Thoreau observed more than a century ago. His words—the motto of the Wilderness Society—should inspire us all.

Janet Flanner
(March 13, 1892 — November 7, 1978)

For fifty years, from 1925 to 1975, Janet Flanner sent her "Letter from Paris" to the *New Yorker,* signed with the androgynous, impersonal "Genet." (The name was selected because editor Harold Ross thought it was the French equivalent of Janet). From the ripening of mushrooms and the gender of the automobile to the death of D. H. Lawrence and the mocking of Nazi radio propaganda, in her letters Flanner blended personal details with political, social, and cultural commentary.

She invented a "formula which dealt not with political news itself but with the effect public political news had on private lives." Readers loved her elegant style, her witty aphorisms, and her crisp observations. About a womanizer she had known, she quipped: "I cannot tell you how many women he has ruined and delighted."

She could be malicious, particularly about the social scene. A recent Paris party was unusual, she reported, in that it "featured only good food and good friends. Among the latter was Miss Dolly Wilde in the habilments of her uncle, Oscar Wilde, and looking both important and earnest." The war years brought a new tone into her writing. On December 7, 1940, she noted sadly that "Paris is now the capital of limbo."

How odd that a young woman born in Indianapolis to Quaker parents would live most of her life in Paris, which she called "the most capital capital of the world." After the University of Chicago expelled her for being a "rebellious influence," she worked briefly as a movie critic, then moved to Paris, where she planned to become another Edith Wharton. Instead she watched history unfold and commented that "history looks queer when you're standing close to it, watching where it is coming from and how it is being made."

In 1959, she was elected to the American Institute of Arts and Letters. "How little such idle honors mean," she wrote a friend. "Only one's work can have counted and what one thinks of it. I think little because it has been ephemeral. I should have used my talent seriously for good books. Alas . . ."

Still, the autumn had always been her favorite time of year. In her last days, she sat re-reading her *Paris Journals.* Sometimes she would laugh at a particular turn of phrase. "I am enjoying my own writing best of all!" she would say.

Sunday
10

Monday
11

◑ *Tuesday*
12

Wednesday
13

Thursday
14

Purim begins at sunset

Friday
15

Saturday
16

February						
S	M	T	W	T	F	S
				1	2	3
4	5	6	7	8	9	10
11	12	13	14	15	16	17
18	19	20	21	22	23	24
25	26	27	28	29		

March
1996

April						
S	M	T	W	T	F	S
	1	2	3	4	5	6
7	8	9	10	11	12	13
14	15	16	17	18	19	20
21	22	23	24	25	26	27
28	29	30				

Sunday
17
St. Patrick, born 457   Mothering Sunday (UK)

Monday
18

Tuesday
19

Wednesday
20

Ovid, b. 43 B.C.
Henrik Ibsen, b. 1828
Friedrich Hölderlin, b. 1770
Nikolai Gogol, b. 1809
Spring Equinox, 3:04 am EST

Thursday
21

Friday
22

Saturday
23

February						
S	M	T	W	T	F	S
				1	2	3
4	5	6	7	8	9	10
11	12	13	14	15	16	17
18	19	20	21	22	23	24
25	26	27	28	29		

March
1996

April						
S	M	T	W	T	F	S
	1	2	3	4	5	6
7	8	9	10	11	12	13
14	15	16	17	18	19	20
21	22	23	24	25	26	27
28	29	30				

He is one of our most cherished authors. Stendhal said it was worth the agony of learning Latin solely in order to read him. Milton ranked him among his three favorite writers. In his own day, Publius Ovidius Naso—Ovid—was, by his own admission, "known throughout the world." His verse shows up in graffiti scrawled on the walls at Pompeii.

As a youth Ovid took up politics at his father's behest, but soon abandoned the "wordy forum" for a poet's life. His father was appalled. "Why try a useless task? Homer himself had no money to leave!" But poetry seemed to course through the young man's veins. Whenever he tried to write prose, Ovid once said, "a poem would come, of its own accord, into the right meter, and what I tried to say ended up in verse."

Ovid
(March 20, 43 B.C. — late 17 or early 18 A.D.)

In contrast to his more sober contemporaries, Virgil and Horace, Ovid wrote often about the lighter side of life. In *On Cosmetics* he offered recipes for skin care. In the *Art of Love*, a series of didactic poems on the art of seduction, he told men where to find women in Rome and told women how to attract men. (Never let them see you without makeup, he warned, and don't laugh if your teeth are bad.) He followed this with yet another didactic collection, *Remedies for Love*, in which he explained how to fall out of love once you had fallen into it.

In his forties Ovid undertook his most innovative work, *The Metamorphoses*, an epic poem calculated to rival Virgil's best work. Ovid's sweeping tale ranges across time and geography, and recounts many of our best known myths. The poem itself metamorphosed as he worked on it. "My spirit is moved to sing of shapes changed into new bodies," Ovid writes at the start of *The Metamorphoses*. "Gods, inspire my undertaking (for you have changed it too)."

But just as he was finishing the poem, Ovid was banished from Rome by the Emperor Augustus—presumably because of his libertine writings. (Ovid would refute the charge by claiming his life was pure, while his Muse, licentious.) He spent the last decade of his life in exile in Romania, where the winters were so cold his wine had to be chopped into servings. Throughout these bitter years, poetry sustained him. "My art is still my companion and my joy," he proclaimed. "Over that Caesar could not get jurisdiction."

Robert Frost

(March 26, 1874 — January 29, 1963)

His public pose was that of a New England farmer poet who wrote verses so accessible that every school child studied, memorized, and recited them. All of Robert Frost's poems, including "Mending Wall," "The Road Not Taken," and "Nothing Gold Can Stay" sound best when read aloud. That was his intention. "I alone of English writers," proclaimed Robert Frost, "have consciously set myself to make music out of what I may call the sound of sense."

Robert Frost rejected the free verse that was in fashion and created a new kind of poetry—a revolutionary blank verse gathered by his ear into rhythmic sentence sounds. He knew his own worth. "To be perfectly frank," he wrote, "I am one of the most notable craftsmen of my time."

Some of his poems, like "Fire and Ice," are quite short, distilling the essence of experience into a few precise lines. Other poems, like "Home Burial," are dramatic dialogues that rival the Greek tragedies in evoking the terrible pain of loss. In "Home Burial," which was written after the death of his four-year-old son, Frost created a masterpiece of artistic form. "There are two types of realist," he said, "the one who offers a good deal of dirt with his potato to show that it is a real one; and the one who is satisfied with the potato brushed clean . . . To me, the thing that art does for life is to clean it, to strip it to form."

Although he's generally considered a poet from New England, Frost was born in San Francisco and was named after the Confederate hero Robert E. Lee. He grew up in Massachusetts and New Hampshire. In 1895 he married Elinor White, his high school sweetheart, and they had six children. Like his contemporaries Ezra Pound and T. S. Eliot, he went abroad to find a climate receptive to his art and to gain the recognition he felt he deserved. Public success and honors soon followed. While the Nobel Prize eluded him, he won the Pulitzer Prize four times as well as countless other honors. His private life, though, was marked by tragedy. He grieved over the death of a daughter and his wife and the suicide of his son. Guilt plagued him. Had he sacrificed his family on the altar of art?

He never stopped working. From his Boston hospital bed two days before he died, he worked on a new poem. He knew he was in his last hours, and poetry for him had always been "a momentary stay against confusion."

Sunday
24
Olive Schreiner, b. 1855

Monday
25

Flannery O'Connor, b. 1925

 ### Tuesday
26

Robert Frost, b. 1874
Tennessee Williams, b. 1911

Wednesday
27

Thursday
28

Maxim Gorky, b. (Gregorian calendar) 1928

Friday
29

Saturday
30
Sean O'Casey, b. 1880

February						
S	M	T	W	T	F	S
				1	2	3
4	5	6	7	8	9	10
11	12	13	14	15	16	17
18	19	20	21	22	23	24
25	26	27	28	29		

March
1996

April						
S	M	T	W	T	F	S
	1	2	3	4	5	6
7	8	9	10	11	12	13
14	15	16	17	18	19	20
21	22	23	24	25	26	27
28	29	30				

Sunday
31
Palm Sunday

Monday
1

Edmond Rostand, b. 1868

Tuesday
2

H. C. Andersen, b. 1805
Giacomo Girolamo Casanova, b. 1725

Wednesday ○
3

Washington Irving, b. 1783
Passover begins at sunset

Thursday
4

Friday
5

Good Friday

Saturday
6

February						
S	M	T	W	T	F	S
					1	2	3
4	5	6	7	8	9	10
11	12	13	14	15	16	17
18	19	20	21	22	23	24
25	26	27	28	29		

March/April
1996

April						
S	M	T	W	T	F	S
	1	2	3	4	5	6
7	8	9	10	11	12	13
14	15	16	17	18	19	20
21	22	23	24	25	26	27
28	29	30				

The man we know as Casanova was born in Venice of actor parents. On his deathbed, his father made him promise never to become an actor. If we can believe Casanova's *Memoirs*, his life was epic theatre, and he was the star.

Casanova claims that his first memories are of his grandmother who took him to a sorceress to cure him of chronic and severe nosebleeds. The sorceress's methods included putting him in a trunk, rubbing him with ointments, pronouncing lamentations and promising him that a "charming lady" would visit him and that if he could keep it a secret, he would be cured. A radiant "fairy queen" appeared to him and his nosebleeds soon decreased.

He became a major player in European politics—a familiar figure in backrooms, bars, and boudoirs. The victim of a political intrigue (he slept with the French Ambassador's mistress who happened to be a nun),

Giacomo Girolamo Casanova
(April 2, 1725 — June 4, 1798)

he was incarcerated on the top floor of the Doge's Palace in the Piazza San Marco. The prison, called the "Leads" because of its lead roofing, could not hold Casanova, and he devised a daring escape.

In France, using the title the "Chevalier de Seingalt," he traveled in a carriage for the first time and since he was accustomed only to water travel, he became "land-sick." He played many roles—entrepreneur, con man, go-between, spy, man of letters, priest, violinist, lover, exploiter and, occasionally, saviour of women. "To cultivate the pleasures of my senses was throughout my life my main preoccupation," he wrote."I have never had any more important objective."

It's largely forgotten that Casanova's other occupation was writing. Throughout his life, he published poems, essays, works on mathematics, and etymology. He had hoped to become a best-selling author with his science fiction novel, *Icosameron*. The novel failed, but two years later, at sixty-five, he wrote his *Memoirs* in which he told the truth about himself and recorded the social history of the eighteenth century. The *Memoirs* made him famous. They have been translated into over twenty languages, although the work is still banned in some countries.

At fifty-eight, Casanova wrote a friend that "winter approaches; and if I think of becoming again an adventurer, I begin to laugh when looking at myself in the mirror." He lived fifteen more years and after his death, his name endured, becoming a universal description of a type.

Sadly, or perhaps ironically, Casanova died alone with only his faithful fox terrier Finette by his side.

He was born almost two and a half centuries ago and his poetry is not in fashion today. His words, though, have much to say to a world teetering on the brink of the twenty-first century. "The world is too much with us, late and soon," he wrote. "Getting and spending, we lay waste our powers; Little we see in Nature that is ours; We have given our hearts away, a sordid boon!"

Influenced by the French Revolution and the writings of Rousseau, Wordsworth rebelled against the Neoclassic idea of poetry as "a mirror held up to nature." The "mind of man" was "my haunt," he wrote, and the "main region of my song."

Later known as the poet who introduced Romanticism into England and the poet who turned the Lake District into the capital of poetry, Wordsworth could not in his own lifetime make enough money writing poetry to support himself or his family. Since he

William Wordsworth
(April 7, 1770 — April 13, 1850)

believed that poetry was "emotion recollected in tranquillity," he lived, too, with the constant fear that his deep well of remembrance would run dry, worrying that "when age comes on, / May scarcely see at all."

What is a poet, Wordsworth asks? Someone "endowed with more lively sensibility, more enthusiasm and tenderness, who has a greater knowledge of human nature, and a more comprehensive soul, than are supposed to be common . . ." Nothing was too ordinary, too common, or too humble to be the subject of Wordsworth's poetry. He wrote of golden daffodils, curling smoke, rushing streams, grazing cattle, and boys in white-sleeved shirts, writing with reverent piety and exuberant self-confidence. "I know not any thing which will not come within the scope of my plan," he said ambitiously.

He never doubted his gift. Through illness, fatigue, the deaths of three of his children, Wordsworth worked. He revised constantly, crossing out, adding new words, still rewriting his poems while the printers ran off the early sheets. And yet he was capable of composing the lovely *Tintern Abbey* entirely in his mind on a long ramble with his sister, "not a line of it was altered, and not any part of it written down till I reached Bristol," he said.

His friend Samuel Taylor Coleridge called him "the best poet of the age." William Hazlitt said that reading his *Lyrical Ballads* was like "the first welcome breath of spring." Late in life, he was honored as England's Poet Laureate. Stricken by pleurisy brought on by a long walk in a cutting northeast wind, William Wordsworth died on April 13, 1850, just as the clock struck noon.

Sunday
7

William Wordsworth, b. 1770   *Gabriela Mistral, b. 1889*   Daylight Saving Time begins   Easter Sunday

Monday
8

Easter Monday (Canada, UK)

Tuesday
9

Wednesday
10

Clare Boothe Luce, b. 1903

Thursday
11

Friday
12

Saturday
13
Samuel Beckett, b. 1906

March						
S	M	T	W	T	F	S
					1	2
3	4	5	6	7	8	9
10	11	12	13	14	15	16
17	18	19	20	21	22	23
24	25	26	27	28	29	30
31						

April
1996

May						
S	M	T	W	T	F	S
			1	2	3	4
5	6	7	8	9	10	11
12	13	14	15	16	17	18
19	20	21	22	23	24	25
26	27	28	29	30	31	

Sunday
14

Monday
15

Henry James, b. 1843

Tuesday
16

Anatole France, b. 1844
J. M. Synge, b. 1871
Holocaust Remembrance Day

Wednesday
17

Isak Dinesen, b. 1885
Thornton Wilder, b. 1897

Thursday
18

Friday
19

José Echegaray, b. 1832
Patriots' Day

Saturday
20

March						
S	M	T	W	T	F	S
					1	2
3	4	5	6	7	8	9
10	11	12	13	14	15	16
17	18	19	20	21	22	23
24	25	26	27	28	29	30
31						

April
1996

May						
S	M	T	W	T	F	S
			1	2	3	4
5	6	7	8	9	10	11
12	13	14	15	16	17	18
19	20	21	22	23	24	25
26	27	28	29	30	31	

At his death in 1924, the French surrealists lampooned him as "A Corpse." His work, they implied, had long been dead. Poet Paul Valéry decried the superficial content of his books. A decade earlier, André Gide had accused Anatole France of creating facile work.

France himself once remarked that he was too bold for his own time and would, to later eyes, seem too timid. He was in many ways an anachronism: a skeptic in an age of positivism, an anticleric in a time of devout belief, a nineteenth-century humanist in an era of automobiles and machine guns. But there was nothing anachronistic about his passion for words.

He literally grew up among words, surrounded by books and writers in his father's Parisian bookshop. At age eight he composed a series of maxims for his mother and began translating Virgil's first eclogue. At ten he claimed that nothing in life rivalled the beauty of correcting proofs. He was still a child when he wrote his first poem.

Anatole France
(April 16, 1844 — October 12, 1924)

But if success later came easily to Anatole France (his last novel sold 60,000 copies in six weeks), it eluded him at first. For a while he earned a living writing prefaces and encyclopedia articles and working in a library. His father said he did nothing but scribble.

He was closest to his mother. Women, in fact, were vital to France throughout his career. His earliest poems recount his unrequited loves. Later he married and had a daughter on whom he doted; her childhood inspired parts of his autobiographical novel *My Friend's Book*, a work that almost certainly influenced Proust.

But France's wife objected to his writing, and one day, after an especially vicious quarrel, the author, wearing a dressing gown and slippers, seized his writing materials and walked out on her. Later he took up with a married woman, Léontine Arman, to whom he remained attached until her death in 1910. Unlike his wife, Mme. Arman pushed France to write. Although Mme. Arman never left her husband, Albert Arman did not mind his wife's affair, and the three often travelled contentedly together.

In his best fiction France proved himself, along with fellow novelists Stendhal, Zola, and Balzac, to be an astute judge of nineteenth-century French society. In 1921 he received the Nobel Prize for literature. But France knew better than anyone the difficulty of his art. "One says nothing in a book of what one would like to say," he observed. "It is impossible to express oneself."

Vladimir Nabokov
(April 22, 1899 — July 5, 1977)

His Russian boyhood was an idyll: a rich and loving family, two homes—city and country—in St. Petersburg, a parade of servants, a mother who read him bedtime stories in three different languages.

And then it ended. The Bolshevik Revolution of 1917 brusquely cancelled Vladimir Nabokov's two-million dollar inheritance, his butterfly-chasing rambles through the fields, his adolescent crush on a girl to whom he wrote hundreds of poems. As the ship bearing him to safety pulled out of Yalta harbor, machine-gun fire strafed its hull. For the rest of his life Nabokov yearned for the Russia he had lost. Nostalgia, he observed drily, is "an insane companion."

"A colored spiral in a small ball of glass, this is how I see my own life," he said. From Russia he fled to Europe, and from Europe to the United States, where he arrived in 1940 and remained for the next two decades. In America, he recalled, "I quit smoking and started to munch molasses candy instead." His weight soared to 200 pounds. "I am one-third American—good American flesh keeping me warm and safe."

Soon after his arrival, Harvard awarded Nabokov a research fellowship as a lepidopterist. (He described a dozen new butterfly varieties in his lifetime, including one named after himself). But writing was his chief occupation. The publication in 1944 of his book *Nikolai Gogol* earned Nabokov a professorship in comparative literature at Cornell University. Years later he reflected, "I amassed an invaluable amount of exciting information in analyzing a dozen novels for my students."

He completed three novels during his years in America, the most famous of them *Lolita*, his shocking tale of an older man's passion for a twelve-year-old girl. Nabokov wrote most of the book while driving cross-country in a Buick on a butterfly-hunting expedition with his wife. *Lolita* scandalized readers when it appeared in 1955. In a disclaimer to the book, Nabokov declared, "I've no general ideas to exploit, I just like composing riddles with elegant solutions."

As a novelist Nabokov became a matchless inventor of realities, perhaps because the Bolshevik Revolution had robbed him of the one reality he adored. "The good writer is first of all an enchanter," he once said. In his own, dazzlingly complex novels, Nabokov transformed "our vision of the imagination," writes critic Robert Alter. ". . . and that is precisely what the novelistic enterprise, from the seventeenth century to our own age, has at its best achieved."

Sunday
21
Charlotte Brontë, b. 1816

Monday
22

Vladimir Nabokov, b. 1899
Madame de Staël, b. 1766

Tuesday
23

William Shakespeare, b. 1564
Bernard Malamud, b. 1914

Wednesday
24

Anthony Trollope, b. 1815

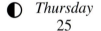 Thursday
25

Friday
26

National Arbor Day

Saturday
27
Mary Wollstonecraft, b. 1759

March						
S	M	T	W	T	F	S
					1	2
3	4	5	6	7	8	9
10	11	12	13	14	15	16
17	18	19	20	21	22	23
24	25	26	27	28	29	30
31						

April
1996

May						
S	M	T	W	T	F	S
			1	2	3	4
5	6	7	8	9	10	11
12	13	14	15	16	17	18
19	20	21	22	23	24	25
26	27	28	29	30	31	

Sunday
28

Monday
29

Tuesday
30

Wednesday
1

Thursday
2

Friday ○
3

Mikhail Bulgakov, b. 1891
William Inge, b. 1913
Niccolò Machiavelli, b. 1469

Saturday
4

March						
S	M	T	W	T	F	S
					1	2
3	4	5	6	7	8	9
10	11	12	13	14	15	16
17	18	19	20	21	22	23
24	25	26	27	28	29	30
31						

April/May
1996

May						
S	M	T	W	T	F	S
			1	2	3	4
5	6	7	8	9	10	11
12	13	14	15	16	17	18
19	20	21	22	23	24	25
26	27	28	29	30	31	

Mikhail Bulgakov
(May 3, 1891 — March 10, 1940)

While laboring to pass his university exams in 1912, twenty-one-year-old Mikhail Bulgakov showed his sister some stories he had written. "You'll see," he promised her. "I'll become a writer."

But Mikhail Bulgakov became a physician first. Lured by medicine's "splendid" calling and by the secrets of the microscope, he graduated from the Medical Faculty of Kiev University in 1916 and worked as a doctor for the next three years.

Meanwhile, he continued to write. In 1913 he composed a brief play for his own wedding. ("Why shouldn't they get married?" a character asks. "They'll live in the bathroom.") In 1919 he had his first short story published. The event so thrilled him that Bulgakov rashly chose to quit his medical career and take up writing fulltime. He never practiced medicine again.

For years he sustained himself and his wife by writing newspaper stories for the Moscow press. The experience taught him to "hate editors. I hate them now and will hate them until the end of my life," he declared in 1926. His first critical and popular success was his 1925 novel *The White Guard*, an account of Bulgakov's native Kiev during the Russian Civil War. He began the book one night after waking from a nightmare about a snowstorm. "That was how I started writing my novel," he said. "I described the snowstorm from my dream."

Despite his triumph with *The White Guard* and with the many plays he wrote throughout the 1920s and '30s for the Moscow Art Theatre, Bulgakov's fortunes rose and fell. He divorced and remarried twice, slipped in and out of favor with the Soviet regime, and struggled, always, to make ends meet.

His most famous work, *The Master and Margarita*, consumed much of the last decade of Bulgakov's life. He despaired so over the book that at one point he tore the manuscript in half and burned most of it. Three years later he resumed work on the complicated novel, which tells the story of a four-day visit to Moscow by the devil. Bulgakov worked on the book right up until his death, in 1940, from kidney failure.

During his last, tortured days Bulgakov subsisted mainly on lemon juice. On March 6, 1940, he told his wife, "It's true that I'm dying—what I would have written after *The Master and Margarita*!" Four days later Bulgakov succumbed. The novel he had called his "last word," his "sunset" book, was not released until 1966—a quarter century after the author's death. Only then, with the publication of *The Master and Margarita*, did Mikhail Bulgakov at last achieve the glory he had sought for so long.

Mari Sandoz

(May 11, 1896 — March 6, 1966)

The oldest child of Swiss immigrant homesteaders, Mari Sandoz grew up in the sandhills of northwestern Nebraska on the Niobrara River, a stark, desolate region on the edge of Indian Country. Around the kitchen table of an evening, she listened as her father and "buffalo-hunting Indians, the old traders, trappers, and general frontiersmen" swapped stories over cups of strong black coffee. Through the stories they told ran a name, "like a painted strip of rawhide in a braided rope," she said, the name of Curly, the light-haired boy, who became Crazy Horse, the great chief, the Strange Man of the Oglalas.

Mari Sandoz's *Crazy Horse* is a classic work of biography and an enduring epic saga of both a man and a people. She spent years researching in government archives, took a 3,000-mile trip through Sioux country, and interviewed the friends and relatives of Crazy Horse who were still alive. She wrote the book from the viewpoint of the Indians, attempting "to say some of the things of the Indian for which there are no white-man words, suggest something of his innate nature, something of his relationship to the earth and the sky and all that is between."

Crazy Horse was her fourth book. During her early years of struggle, she supported herself by teaching, and received more than 1,000 rejections for her short stories. Her first book, *Old Jules*, a biography of her father, was rejected fourteen times before it was finally published in 1935. Sandoz wrote twenty-one books, including the epic *Cheyenne Autumn* which was turned into a movie that bore no resemblance to her well-documented work. Her reputation rests on her six-volume Great Plains Series which includes *Old Jules, Crazy Horse, Cheyenne Autumn, The Beaver Men, The Buffalo Hunters*, and *The Cattlemen*. Almost all of her writing was based on meticulous historical research which often debunked popular western heroes like Wild Bill Hickok, whom she considered a murdering madman.

In 1943 she moved to Greenwich Village, but she traveled and lectured widely, living for months at a time in her beloved West. In her last book, *The Battle of the Little Bighorn*, written when she was suffering terribly from bone cancer, she presented the Indian's version of the battle, drawing on exclusive material given to her by the Sioux and Cheyenne.

Her books are potent testimony to her art, but Mari Sandoz was a modest woman, and in telling the stories of the Indians, she hoped that she had not failed "too miserably."

Sunday
5

Monday
6

Sigmund Freud, b. 1856
May Day Holiday (UK)

Tuesday
7

Rabindranath Tagore, b. 1861
Edward Lear, b. 1812

Wednesday
8

Thursday
9

Benito Pérez Galdós, b. 1843

 Friday
10

Saturday
11
Mari Sandoz, b. 1896

April						
S	M	T	W	T	F	S
	1	2	3	4	5	6
7	8	9	10	11	12	13
14	15	16	17	18	19	20
21	22	23	24	25	26	27
28	29	30				

May
1996

June						
S	M	T	W	T	F	S
						1
2	3	4	5	6	7	8
9	10	11	12	13	14	15
16	17	18	19	20	21	22
23	24	25	26	27	28	29
30						

Sunday
12
Mothers' Day   *Daphne du Maurier, b. 1907*

Monday
13

Tuesday
14

Dante Alighieri, b. 1265

Wednesday
15

Katharine Anne Porter, b. 1890
L. Frank Baum, b. 1856

Thursday
16

Friday
17

Saturday
18
Armed Forces Day

April						
S	M	T	W	T	F	S
		1	2	3	4	5	6
7	8	9	10	11	12	13
14	15	16	17	18	19	20
21	22	23	24	25	26	27
28	29	30				

May
1996

June						
S	M	T	W	T	F	S
						1
2	3	4	5	6	7	8
9	10	11	12	13	14	15
16	17	18	19	20	21	22
23	24	25	26	27	28	29
30						

Daphne du Maurier had the melodious name, the blonde, blue-eyed beauty, and the privileged background of a romance heroine. Her grandfather was George du Maurier, the *Punch* cartoonist and author of *Trilby* and *Peter Ibbetson* and her father was Gerald du Maurier, the famous actor-manager. She was not the boy her father wanted, but the middle daughter in a family of three girls. She desired desperately to be a boy, and yet she was a girl and what would she do with her life, she wondered. In a piece of juvenilia she wrote about a boy "who is searching for happiness, at least not exactly happiness, but that something that is somewhere, you know. You feel it and you miss it and it beckons and you can't reach it . . . I don't think anyone can find it on this earth."

She escaped into writing, immersing herself in the characters, losing herself in the

Daphne du Maurier
(May 12, 1907 — April 18, 1989)

story. In her classic novel, *Rebecca*, her nameless heroine, the second Mrs. De Winter, continues the search for happiness. "Last night I dreamt I went to Manderley again..." she says in the unforgettable opening lines of the book.

Daphne du Maurier, her husband, and three children lived in a seventy-room manor house on the Cornwall coast called Menabilly, the model for *Rebecca's* Manderley. In addition to *Rebecca*, du Maurier wrote thirty-seven books, including *Jamaica Inn*, *Frenchman's Creek*, and *My Cousin Rachel*. Alfred Hitchcock based his suspense movie *The Birds* on one of her short stories. "What is a suspense novel?" she asked. "People in doubt, people mystified, people groping on their way from one situation to another, from childhood to middle age, from joy to sorrow—these are the figures in a true suspense novel. They are traveling along a road of uncertainty toward an unseen goal."

Writing comes from within, she once said. "A character or an idea has to grow like a seed and take possession . . . it's something to do with one's own development and passage through life." In her brilliant 1993 biography, Margaret Forster reveals that Daphne du Maurier traveled along the same road of uncertainty as her characters, finding solace and life itself in the creation of her fiction. "Daphne du Maurier, Dame of the British Empire," says Forster, "a world-wide and enduring bestselling author for nearly fifty years, had a loving family, devoted friends, and everything, it would seem, a woman could possibly have wanted, but if she could not write all this seemed worthless."

Ralph Waldo Emerson
(May 25, 1803 — April 27, 1882)

How many times have you heard these familiar phrases? Nothing great is ever achieved without enthusiasm. The reward of a thing well done, is to have done it. Hitch your wagon to a star. A foolish consistency is the hobgoblin of little minds. Keep cool; it will all be one a hundred years hence.

The author of these sentences was, of course, Ralph Waldo Emerson, perhaps one of the most quotable figures in American literary history. Emerson hated quotations. Tell me what you know, he would say. He also said, "Next to the originator of a good sentence is the first quoter of it."

There was little sign in Emerson's youth that he would become American's first great literary hero. The son of a Boston minister, he was an indifferent student, managing only a rank of thirty in a class of fifty-nine at Harvard College. He attended Harvard Divinity School, married Ellen Tucker, a wealthy merchant's daughter, and became the pastor of Boston's Old North Church. After his wife died in 1831 of tuberculosis, Emerson experienced a spiritual awakening which formed the basis for his philosophy of self-reliance. God existed in the individual soul, he believed. He resigned from his ministry and took a long trip to Europe where he formed significant friendships with William Wordsworth, Samuel Taylor Coleridge, and Thomas Carlyle.

For the rest of his life, Emerson earned his living lecturing and writing books (*Nature, Essays, The Conduct of Life, Society and Solitude*). He spoke out publicly and courageously against the evils of slavery. Although he's remembered for his essays and his philosophy, Emerson always thought of himself as a poet. He strived to create poetry as "new as foam and as old as the rock," but his ambitions were greater than his achievements.

He could be withering in his estimate of other writers. About Jane Austen he wrote, "Never was life so pinched and narrow. The one problem in the mind of the writer is . . . marriageableness . . . Suicide is more respectable." Hawthorne's writing was "not good for anything, and this is a tribute to the man."

He was our national nanny, raising a generation of writers and generations of Americans to full adulthood. His own thoughts and words, and his philosophy of Transcendentalism, as filtered through Thoreau, Melville, Whitman, and Dickinson, have permeated and shaped our national consciousness, proving Emerson's belief that "There is properly no history; only biography."

Sunday
19
Lorraine Hansberry, b. 1930

Monday
20

Honoré Balzac, b. 1799
Victoria Day (Canada)

Tuesday
21

Wednesday
22

Thursday
23

Friday
24

◑ Saturday
25
Ralph Waldo Emerson, b. 1803   *Raymond Carver, b. 1938*

April
S M T W T F S
1 2 3 4 5 6
7 8 9 10 11 12 13
14 15 16 17 18 19 20
21 22 23 24 25 26 27
28 29 30

May
1996

June
S M T W T F S
1
2 3 4 5 6 7 8
9 10 11 12 13 14 15
16 17 18 19 20 21 22
23 24 25 26 27 28 29
30

Sunday
26

Monday
27

Rachel Carson, b. 1907
Dashiell Hammett, b. 1894
John Cheever, b. 1912
Memorial Day
Spring Bank Holiday (UK ex. Scotland)

Tuesday
28

Patrick White, b. 1912

Wednesday
29

Thursday
30

Friday
31

Walt Whitman, b. 1819

Saturday ○
1

April						
S	M	T	W	T	F	S
	1	2	3	4	5	6
7	8	9	10	11	12	13
14	15	16	17	18	19	20
21	22	23	24	25	26	27
28	29	30				

May/June
1996

June						
S	M	T	W	T	F	S
						1
2	3	4	5	6	7	8
9	10	11	12	13	14	15
16	17	18	19	20	21	22
23	24	25	26	27	28	29
30						

Fourteen robins killed by the pesticide DDT inspired Rachel Carson's *Silent Spring*, published in 1962. In the book's apocalyptic first chapter, she wrote: "No witchcraft, no enemy action had silenced the rebirth of new life in this stricken world. The people had done it themselves."

A half-million people bought hard-cover copies of *Silent Spring*. The book prompted passage of new laws around the world that controlled the use of pesticides. Based on painstaking, meticulous research, the book took Carson four-and-a-half years to write. She usually wrote at night when she could work undisturbed, penning her rough drafts in longhand, revising endlessly. A writer must never "impose upon the subject," she said. The writer's discipline was "to learn to be still and listen to what his subject has to tell him."

Rachel Carson
(May 27, 1907 — April 14, 1964)

A solitary child with dark brown, deep-set eyes, she grew up on a sixty-five-acre farm in Springdale, Pennsylvania. She learned a reverence for all forms of life from her mother and from Beatrix Potter books. When flies or spiders appeared in the house, they were released outside, and Rachel convinced her brother to give up shooting rabbits. She was never bored. There was always something new to experience—a garter snake shedding its skin, the care of orphaned robins, the rushing roar of a conch shell.

There were no writers in her family, and she had no idea why she wanted to be one. She majored in English at the Pennsylvania College for Women, but became fascinated with her biology class. She chose biology over English and went on to graduate work at Johns Hopkins University. It was poetry, though, that inspired her. Tennyson's poem "Locksley Hall," and the lines "roaring seaward, and I go," prompted her lifelong study of the sea.

She combined a scholar's exactitude and dedication with an artist's compassion and sensibility. At the Marine Biological Laboratory at Woods Hole, Massachusetts, she watched young mullets and stood "knee-deep in that racing water and at the time could barely see those darting, silver bits of life for my tears."

Her work at Wood's Hole led to her first best seller, *The Sea Around Us*. Her last book, published posthumously, was *The Sense of Wonder*. A courageous, spiritual writer, she believed there was "symbolic as well as actual beauty in the migration of birds; in the ebb and flow of the tides; in the folded bud ready for the spring."

Marguerite Yourcenar
(June 8, 1903 — December 17, 1987)

As a young girl, Marguerite Yourcenar sensed that she was, in her own words, "important, even very important." She lived to fulfill that prophesy.

She was a serious child. Her mother died ten days after Marguerite's birth, in Belgium, in 1903, and the infant was watched over from afar by a woman Yourcenar later assumed had been her mother's lover. It was Yourcenar's French father, however, a compulsive gambler and devotee of literature, who raised the child and taught her to love travel and learning. In place of toys and dolls, Yourcenar played with words. At a precocious age she began to recite poetry; in her teens she studied Latin and Greek with her father, who served as her sole tutor. At sixteen she composed a poetic drama, *Icarus*.

In her twenties Marguerite Yourcenar discovered most of the themes she would spend the rest of her career exploring, including the life and times of the Roman Emperor Hadrian. She began writing a version of Hadrian's life when she was twenty-six, but soon abandoned it. Two decades later she returned to the subject with her 1951 masterpiece, *Memoirs of Hadrian*. Author Edmund White has termed this book "one of the great same-sex love stories of all time." Yourcenar was moved to write about the Emperor after reading a letter by Gustave Flaubert in which the French novelist observed, "There was a unique moment between Cicero and Marcus Aurelius when the gods no longer existed and Christ had not yet emerged and humanity was all alone." In her passionate tale of Hadrian's life, Yourcenar sought to recreate this singular moment.

The writer spent most of her own life living quietly with her companion Grace Frick, an American, on a remote island off the Maine coast. It was a curious spot for a woman whom Edmund White regards as "the most thoroughly French of all modern French writers." Nevertheless, Yourcenar felt at home on the secluded island. "It is somewhat as if I were in the United States while not being there," she told a friend.

Bent on maintaining her privacy, Yourcenar instructed Frick to keep journalists and other curiosity seekers at bay so that she could get on with her work. At her death, Yourcenar's personal papers were sealed until the year 2037. "Nothing is more secret than a woman's existence," she once explained. "Life is far more complex than any of its possible definitions. Every simplified vision of life always risks being crude."

Sunday
2
Thomas Hardy, b. 1840

Monday
3

Holiday (Rep. of Ireland)

Tuesday
4

Wednesday
5

Federico García Lorca, b. 1898

Thursday
6

Friday
7

◗ Saturday
8
Marguerite Yourcenar, b. 1903

May						
S	M	T	W	T	F	S
			1	2	3	4
5	6	7	8	9	10	11
12	13	14	15	16	17	18
19	20	21	22	23	24	25
26	27	28	29	30	31	

June
1996

July						
S	M	T	W	T	F	S
	1	2	3	4	5	6
7	8	9	10	11	12	13
14	15	16	17	18	19	20
21	22	23	24	25	26	27
28	29	30	31			

Sunday
9

Monday
10

Tuesday
11

Wednesday
12

Anne Frank, b. 1929
Djuna Barnes, b. 1892

Thursday
13

Fanny Burney, b. 1752
William Butler Yeats, b. 1865

Friday
14

Harriet Beecher Stowe, b. 1811
Flag Day

Saturday ●
15

			May			
S	M	T	W	T	F	S
					1	2	3	4
5	6	7	8	9	10	11
12	13	14	15	16	17	18
19	20	21	22	23	24	25
26	27	28	29	30	31	

June
1996

			July			
S	M	T	W	T	F	S
	1	2	3	4	5	6
7	8	9	10	11	12	13
14	15	16	17	18	19	20
21	22	23	24	25	26	27
28	29	30	31			

Hers was not a propitious start. By the time she was eight, Frances Burney still could not read. Her father nicknamed her "the Old Lady" because she was so shy. At ten she "began scribbling . . . but always in private." On her fifteenth birthday, apparently in deference to her father's expressed opposition to so frivolous an activity as writing, she built a huge bonfire and into it tossed all her manuscripts: "Elegies, Odes, Plays, Songs, Stories, Farces—nay Tragedies and Epic Poems." Also immolated in that dramatic pyre was Fanny Burney's first novel, *The History of Caroline Evelyn.*

Burney returned to the story of Caroline Evelyn a few years later, weaving the lost tale into the first four letters of her next novel, *Evelina,* an epistolary account of a naive girl's encounter with society. Fanny published the book in 1778 with the help of her brother Charles, who went

Fanny Burney
(June 13, 1752 — January 6, 1840)

incognito to a bookseller with his sister's manuscript. *Evelina* was so successful that the novel went into four editions by the end of 1779. Six months after its publication, its twenty-six year old author at last revealed her identity to her father, who was so charmed by his timid daughter's triumph that he proudly introduced Fanny to Dr. Johnson, one of the book's admirers.

In *Evelina,* Burney revealed the derision and scorn to which eighteenth-century British women were typically subjected. "I don't know what the devil a woman lives for after thirty," one male character remarks. "She is only in other folks' way."

In her own life, Fanny Burney knew such prejudice firsthand. Despite the success of both *Evelina* and a subsequent novel, *Cecilia* (1782), Burney's status as a thirty-year old spinster had more bearing on her future than any book she might produce. In 1786, at her family's insistence, Fanny reluctantly accepted a court position—as second keeper of the robes to Queen Charlotte—in order to insure her financial security. The job so depressed her that she nearly went mad, and after five years of servitude she quit.

In later years Burney married happily, bore a son, continued to write, and survived breast cancer. (Her diaries contain a detailed account of the mastectomy she endured in 1821 without anaesthetic.) In all ways her life defied convention.

The timid young woman who at sixteen addressed her diary as "Nobody" died in 1840, at age eighty-seven, a famous novelist. Fanny Burney is buried not at Westminster Abbey, like her male peers, but in an unmarked grave beside her family in the provincial city of Bath.

Mary McCarthy
(June 21, 1912 — October 25, 1989)

Her parents died in the great flu epidemic of 1918. Orphaned at six, for the next five years Mary McCarthy endured a childhood of "almost Dickensian cruelty and squalor." In the house of her great-aunt in Minneapolis, she was beaten with a razor strop to keep her "from getting stuck up," forced to stand outdoors for hours at a time in sub-zero cold, and fed a diet of carrots, parsnips, chicken necks, prunes, and farina.

She was saved by the intervention of her maternal grandfather, who moved her to Seattle and enrolled her in Catholic schools. Her candid, graceful, and often funny memoirs, *Memories of a Catholic Girlhood* and *How I Grew*, tell the story of those painful years. "My laughter was a victory over circumstances," she wrote, "and a kind of pardon."

A novelist, short story writer, memoirist, journalist, and critic, Mary McCarthy earned both exceptional literary achievement and great popular success. Other writers extolled her and feared her. Norman Mailer named her "Our First Lady of Letters." Robert Lowell called her "our Diana, rash to awkwardness." She was a Diana who sometimes dipped her arrows in venom and perhaps envy—writing, for example, that Tennessee Williams's masterpiece, *A Streetcar Named Desire*, "reeks of literary ambition as the apartment reeks of cheap perfume." She attacked Lillian Hellman, proclaiming that every word the playwright wrote "is a lie, including *and* and *the*." Infuriated, Hellman sued her for $2.25 million dollars. Hellman died before the lawsuit was settled.

In *Writing Dangerously*, her splendid biography of Mary McCarthy, Carol Brightman reports that one week after McCarthy's marriage to her second husband, Edmund Wilson, he put her in a "spare room with a typewriter and shut the door." He believed that she had a talent for writing short stories. She did. She produced *The Company She Keeps*, a collection of interconnected stories which drew on her own intellectual and sexual adventures.

In writing fiction, McCarthy said that her method was to take "real plums and put them in an imaginary cake." She plucked the plums from her experiences at Vassar and put them into her novel *The Group*. The novel, which took her eleven years to write, was made into a movie, and by 1991 over five million copies of the book had been sold.

McCarthy rarely talked about death, but she once told a friend, "I cannot bear the thought of that accumulation of so many beautiful things seen and heard, books read and written, and then bang, it's gone, destroyed!" Mary McCarthy died at seventy-seven of lung cancer.

Sunday
16
Fathers' Day

Monday
17

John Hersey, b. 1914

Tuesday
18

Blaise Pascal, b. 1623

Wednesday
19

Lillian Hellman, b. 1905
Summer Solstice, 10:24 pm EDT

Thursday
20

Mary McCarthy, b. 1912

Friday
21

Saturday
22
Erich Maria Remarque, b. 1898

May						
S	M	T	W	T	F	S
				1	2	3	4
5	6	7	8	9	10	11
12	13	14	15	16	17	18
19	20	21	22	23	24	25
26	27	28	29	30	31	

June
1996

July						
S	M	T	W	T	F	S
	1	2	3	4	5	6
7	8	9	10	11	12	13
14	15	16	17	18	19	20
21	22	23	24	25	26	27
28	29	30	31			

Sunday
23

Monday ◑
24

St. John of the Cross, b. 1542

Tuesday
25

Wednesday
26

Pearl Buck, b. 1892

Thursday
27

Helen Keller, b. 1880

Friday
28

Luigi Pirandello, b. 1867

Saturday
29

		May				
S	M	T	W	T	F	S
				1	2	3	4
5	6	7	8	9	10	11
12	13	14	15	16	17	18
19	20	21	22	23	24	25
26	27	28	29	30	31	

June
1996

		July				
S	M	T	W	T	F	S
	1	2	3	4	5	6
7	8	9	10	11	12	13
14	15	16	17	18	19	20
21	22	23	24	25	26	27
28	29	30	31			

Venerabilis P. Fr. Ioannes a Cruce hispanus, B. Virginis Teresa a Iesu Carmelitaru difcalceatorum Matris & Fundatricis primus filius ac fideliffimus coadiutor, diuinis a tur coloquys. Segouia ante imaginem Christi Domini crucem haiulantis orans ab ip

St. John of the Cross
(June 24[?], 1542 — December 14, 1591)

Twice in childhood, Juan de Yepes y Alvarez beheld the Virgin. Once, She appeared to him in a vision after he had fallen into a pond; shortly afterward someone pulled him to safety. He saw Her a second time at the age of twelve, when he plunged into a deep well and nearly drowned. Her presence sustained him until help arrived.

John of Yepes saw the Virgin a third time at the age of thirty-five when, according to his first biographer, She came to him in a dream and told him his trials would soon end. He was by then Friar John of the Cross, and a prisoner, held captive in the city of Toledo, Spain, by a rival faction of his own Carmelite order. Confined for nine months to a six- by ten-foot closet, with no change of clothing and only scraps of bread and fish for food, and repeatedly flogged by captors who recited the *Miserere* as they struck him, John of the Cross endured his ordeal through faith alone. His glimpse of the Virgin gave him hope, and soon after Her miraculous appearance he escaped.

While in jail a sympathetic guard had given him a pen and ink so that he might "compose from time to time a few things profitable to devotion." Friar John used these to write poetry. After his escape he continued to write devotional verse as well as prose for the next several years, composing passages in short snatches and sometimes writing on his knees, out of reverence for his subject. Of the striking images in his poems he explained, "Sometimes God gave them to me and at other times I looked for them myself."

A quiet, solitary man who stood under five feet tall, John of the Cross scorned pride, and to insure humility mortified himself by wearing undergarments of esparto grass and, once, a chain with points that cut into his skin. In his last years he showed signs of sainthood; he gave off aromatic odors and bright lights, and according to witnesses he sometimes levitated.

Throughout his life, as if to relive his harrowing months in jail, John of the Cross sought out cell-like enclosures with narrow windows that opened onto spacious views. Here he would spend hours in revery, enthralled by the beauty of God's creation. If his character is ultimately unknowable to us, his spirit is not. It resides in his poems, as alive and luminous as the landscapes he so adored.

Jean Cocteau
(July 5, 1889 — October 11, 1963)

"**S**ince the age of fifteen I haven't stopped for a minute," Jean Cocteau once said. During his long and busy career the slender Parisian with "electrified hair" explored almost every art: theatre, film, ballet, fiction, poetry, sculpture, and drawing. He even took up drumming in his late twenties. To his mother's charge that he was wasting his time, Cocteau replied, "If some kind person should say to you, 'Isn't your son the leader of a Negro jazz band?', please tell them: 'Yes. We think it's the best job he's ever had.'"

He insisted on calling himself a poet, and he labelled all of his work "poetry." "I have been accused of jumping from branch to branch. Well, I have—but always in the same tree," Cocteau observed. He meant the "tree" of poetry.

He was restless in both art and life. For years he lived a nomadic life, moving from one hotel to another or visiting friends when his money ran out. After his young lover Raymond Radiguet died of typhoid in 1923, a shattered Cocteau began smoking opium. The first five years of his addiction and his attempts at withdrawal were the subject of his 1932 book *Opium: The Diary of an Addict.*

His mother was Cocteau's closest confidante. She indulged him in his childhood, when he was a frail boy fond of lying in bed and dressing in girls' clothes. She eased him through the pain of his father's suicide when Jean was just nine years old, an event that haunted Cocteau for years. His mother remained a powerful force in his life until her death in 1943. Cocteau sent her more than a thousand letters, sometimes three a day.

As an artist Cocteau viewed his development as a series of "moultings"—the discarding of old tastes for new. His most profound "moulting," he said, was World War I, which prompted him to shed the conservatism of his early years and embrace the avant-garde. In all of his many works—from his novels of the 1920s, to his revolutionary ballet *Parade,* to his eloquent film *Beauty and the Beast*—Jean Cocteau tested the bounds of poetry and art.

He died in 1963 and is buried in a chapel whose walls are decorated with murals Cocteau himself designed. "He never seemed old," friends said of him. "The lasting feeling that his work leaves is one of happiness," remarked poet W.H. Auden, "not of course in the sense that it excludes suffering, but because, in it, nothing is rejected, resented or regretted."

○ *Sunday*
30

Monday
1

George Sand, b. 1804
Susan Glaspell, b. 1873
Canada Day

Tuesday
2

Wednesday
3

Franz Kafka, b. 1883

Thursday
4

Nathaniel Hawthorne, b. 1804
Declaration of Independence, 1776

Friday
5

Jean Cocteau, b. 1889

Saturday
6

		May			
S*	M	T	W	T	F	S

May						
S*	M	T	W	T	F	S
			1	2	3	4
5	6	7	8	9	10	11
12	13	14	15	16	17	18
19	20	21	22	23	24	25
26	27	28	29	30	31	

June/July
1996

July						
S	M	T	W	T	F	S
	1	2	3	4	5	6
7	8	9	10	11	12	13
14	15	16	17	18	19	20
21	22	23	24	25	26	27
28	29	30	31			

Sunday
7
Robert A. Heinlein, b. 1907

Monday
8

Tuesday
9

Wednesday
10

Thursday
11

E. B. White, b. 1899

Friday
12

Pablo Neruda, b. 1904
Henry D. Thoreau, b. 1817
Holiday (N. Ireland)

Saturday
13

	June					
S	M	T	W	T	F	S
						1
2	3	4	5	6	7	8
9	10	11	12	13	14	15
16	17	18	19	20	21	22
23	24	25	26	27	28	29
30						

July
1996

	August					
S	M	T	W	T	F	S
				1	2	3
4	5	6	7	8	9	10
11	12	13	14	15	16	17
18	19	20	21	22	23	24
25	26	27	28	29	30	31

On summer nights in southern Missouri the heavens seemed vast and the stars looked bright and close to Robert Anson Heinlein. With his doctor grandfather, he traveled in a horse and buggy, but his heart was already wandering in the stars.

He gobbled up the early science fiction dime novels about boy geniuses who invented fantastic machines and made their fortunes, and then moved on to Edgar Rice Burroughs, Jules Verne, and H. G. Wells. The future fascinated him, and he dreamed of becoming an astronomer.

His classmates at Central High School in Kansas City noted that "he thinks in terms of the fifth dimension, never stopping at the fourth." He graduated from the United States Naval Academy in 1929, served as a gunnery officer on an aircraft carrier, and after contracting tuberculosis retired from the Navy with the rank of lieutenant.

Robert A. Heinlein
(July 7, 1907 — May 8, 1988)

He wrote his first science fiction story in 1939 and sold it to *Astounding Fiction* for a penny a word. He earned seventy dollars. After World War II, he became the first science fiction writer to break into general circulation magazines like *The Saturday Evening Post*. His twenty-six novels and nine collections of shorter fiction have been translated into twenty-eight languages. Four of his novels have been honored with Hugo Awards.

In 1961, his novel *Stranger in a Strange Land* became a cult classic and was adopted by the counter-culture. Michael Valentine Smith, the messianic central character, a man raised by Martians, captured the imagination of a generation hungry for meaning and community. Tragically, Charles Manson read the novel and used it as a model in the creation of his "family" of young female worshippers who practiced group sex and their own murderous version of "discorporating" people.

Some critics revile Heinlein as a hack who wrote dull, boring diatribes. Others call him a visionary genius. All argue over the meaning of his work. Still, *Stranger in a Strange Land* has gone through forty-eight printings since 1979, and Heinlein's word "grok" has entered the dictionary, defined as "to understand thoroughly because of having empathy."

In his youth, Heinlein rode in a horse and buggy and in his old age he flew in the B-1 bomber. His work followed the trajectory of his country. George Slusser writes that "Heinlein's true land is materialist America. Out of its hopes and fears, he has fashioned, perhaps without knowing it, a new circle in hell."

William Makepeace Thackeray
(July 18, 1811 — December 24, 1863)

When he was a boy his head was so big in proportion to his slight figure that his aunt took him to a physician who promptly reassured her, "Don't be alarmed, ma'am. He has a large head, but there's a great deal in it."

At six feet four inches, William Makepeace Thackeray towered over other writers. His talent was equally huge. Charles Dickens was his only rival. When he read Dickens' *Dombey and Son*, Thackeray exclaimed, "There's no writing against this; one hasn't an atom of chance. It's stupendous!"

After years of grubbing as a journalist, writing travel pieces, short stories, criticism, and straight reporting, Thackerary produced his masterpiece with its unforgettable adventuress Becky Sharpe. As he worked on the novel, he wondered "whether this will take—the publishers accept it, and the world read it." The title eluded him. During the middle of the night, a voice whispered to him, and he ran round the room chanting, "Vanity Fair, Vanity Fair, Vanity Fair."

Thackeray's life resembled the Gothic romances he loved as a boy. He was born in Calcutta, India, and at six (following the death of his father), he returned to England alone. Sent off to boarding school, he endured "hard beds, hard words, strange boys bullying" and had his nose broken in a fight. Every night he prayed to "dream of my mother." He entered Cambridge, but did not graduate, and soon married. His wife became hopelessly insane and was institutionalized. Thackeray supported his two daughters by writing. He compared his trade to that of a bootblack. "To do your work honestly, to amuse and instruct your reader . . . to die when your time comes . . ." was his creed.

Charlotte Brontë dedicated *Jane Eyre* to him. "Thackeray is unique," she said. "I can say no more, I will say no less." To Thackeray, fiction was as true as history. The novelist, he believed, should write about "morals and manners."

His novels *Vanity Fair* and *Barry Lyndon,* in particular, continue to amuse and instruct. Ironically, as his fame increased, Thackeray enjoyed the "lionisation" of society, and Charlotte Brontë complained that he mingled too much with the *beau monde* that he had skewered so brilliantly.

Just hours before he died, he corrected proofs of a new novel. When Charles Dickens looked at him in his coffin, "he wondered that the figure he had known in life as one of such noble presence could seem so shrunken and wasted."

Monday
15

Tuesday
16

Wednesday
17

Thursday
18

Friday
19

Saturday
20

July
1996

Sunday
21
Hart Crane, b. 1899   John Gardner, b. 1933   Ernest Hemingway, b. 1899

Monday
22

Tuesday ☽
23

Wednesday
24

Alexandre Dumas, père, b. 1802

Thursday
25

Friday
26

George Bernard Shaw, b. 1856

Saturday
27

		June				
S	M	T	W	T	F	S
						1
2	3	4	5	6	7	8
9	10	11	12	13	14	15
16	17	18	19	20	21	22
23	24	25	26	27	28	29
30						

July
1996

		August				
S	M	T	W	T	F	S
				1	2	3
4	5	6	7	8	9	10
11	12	13	14	15	16	17
18	19	20	21	22	23	24
25	26	27	28	29	30	31

Ernest Hemingway once made a list of all the things he loved to do: "To stay in places and to leave, to trust, to distrust, to no longer believe and to believe again . . . to see what happens, to be out in boats, to sit in a saddle, to watch the snow come, to watch it go, to hear rain on a tent, to know where I can find what I want."

"What he really wanted," his biographer Carlos Baker believed, "was a total immersion in the sensuous experience of living."

Hemingway led a life so vital, a life so packed with incident, adventure, love, and loss that his own story rivals the best of his fiction. He worked as a reporter, drove an ambulance in World War I, ran with the bulls in Spain, hunted game in Africa, hob-nobbed with other members of the "lost generation" in Paris, married four times, and fathered three sons.

Ernest Hemingway
(July 21, 1899 — July 2, 1961)

And, all the time, he worked like a "son-of-a-bitch," he said. His best novels, *The Sun Also Rises, A Farewell to Arms, For Whom the Bell Tolls, The Old Man and the Sea,* and his short stories collected in *The First Forty-Nine Stories,* form the bedrock of countless courses in American literature.

He measured himself against other writers and was determined to win. John Steinbeck said it was as if Hemingway and Faulkner were "fighting for billing on the tombstone." Hemingway bragged that he had beaten Turgenev and de Maupassant, "fought two draws with Mr. Stendhal... But nobody's going to get me in any ring with Mr. Tolstoy unless I'm crazy or I keep getting better."

Not everyone appreciated his prose. Tom Wolfe contended that "Hemingway repeats himself all the time, using 'and' for padding." Faulkner said that Hemingway never used a word "that might send a reader to the dictionary." His clean, unadorned prose style—like this sentence from "Big Two-Hearted River": "Nick swung the rod back over his shoulder and forward, and the line, curving forward, laid the grasshopper down on one of the deep channels in the weeds"—recreated the rhythms of action.

Hemingway once advised his friend Scott Fitzgerald that "when you get the damned hurt, use it." At sixty-two, stricken with diabetes, cirrhosis of the liver, and severe depression, Hemingway wept in despair because he was not able to transfer his hurt to words on a page. On July 2, 1961, in his house in Ketchum, Idaho, he shot himself in the forehead with a double-barrelled shotgun.

Giorgio Vasari
(July 30, 1511 — June 27, 1574)

Few human beings have been more prolific. In just sixty-two years of life, painter, architect, and writer Giorgio Vasari frescoed the walls of palaces and churches throughout Renaissance Italy, designed both the Uffizi Gallery and Michelangelo's tomb, and researched and wrote the monumental biographical compendium *Lives of the Artists.*

He once complained that in order to do so much he had to traipse "like a gypsy throughout Italy." But Vasari could conceive of no other life. He despised only three things, writes critic T.S.R. Boase: "slackness in work, over-indulgence in pleasure, and unreliability." "I hate war," Vasari once remarked, "for it deprives us of the chance of working."

As a boy he studied Latin and drawing. Although he first gained notice for his skill with a pen, it was his talent with a paintbrush that sustained Vasari financially through most of his life. At one point he earned a living by copying worldly works in the Vatican for a secularly-minded Cardinal.

It was in Rome that a group of literary men first suggested to Vasari that he draft a treatise on the lives of famous artists of the day. Because Vasari was himself an artist, and because he could write in the vernacular, he accepted their proposal.

Borrowing from existing biographies and chronicles, church records, inventories, and firsthand accounts "from those who had known them," Vasari compiled his prodigious *Lives of the Artists.* It was weary work. The author later said he persevered only through the encouragement of his friends. When the book finally appeared in 1550, he apologized for its inevitable inaccuracies. "Those that have tried what a thing it is to write, will hold me excused," he said.

But despite its errors of fact and chronology, *Lives* is a masterpiece. Filled with great knowledge and intimate anecdote, and written "in the way that seemed most natural and easy," as Vasari phrased it, the massive work delighted readers in its own time and fixed scholars' views of the Renaissance for the next three centuries.

With *Lives,* Vasari secured the fame he had long craved. His prefatory remarks to the book's second edition might serve to describe himself as well as his subjects. "I shall claim," he wrote, "that with this breath these men have never perished, nor been conquered by death."

Sunday
28
Beatrix Potter, b. 1866   Gerard Manley Hopkins, b. 1844

Monday
29

○ *Tuesday*
30

Giorgio Vasari, b. 1511
Emily Brontë, b. 1818

Wednesday
31

Thursday
1

Herman Melville, b. 1819

Friday
2

James Baldwin, b. 1924

Saturday
3

June						
S	M	T	W	T	F	S
						1
2	3	4	5	6	7	8
9	10	11	12	13	14	15
16	17	18	19	20	21	22
23	24	25	26	27	28	29
30						

July/August
1996

August						
S	M	T	W	T	F	S
				1	2	3
4	5	6	7	8	9	10
11	12	13	14	15	16	17
18	19	20	21	22	23	24
25	26	27	28	29	30	31

Sunday
4
Knut Hamsun, b. 1859

Monday
5

Holiday (Rep. of Ireland)

Tuesday
6

Alfred Lord Tennyson, b. 1809

Wednesday
7

Alice James, b. 1848

Thursday
8

Marjorie Kinnan Rawlings, b. 1896

Friday
9

Saturday
10
Smithsonian Institution's 150th anniversary

July						
S	M	T	W	T	F	S
	1	2	3	4	5	6
7	8	9	10	11	12	13
14	15	16	17	18	19	20
21	22	23	24	25	26	27
28	29	30	31			

August
1996

September						
S	M	T	W	T	F	S
1	2	3	4	5	6	7
8	9	10	11	12	13	14
15	16	17	18	19	20	21
22	23	24	25	26	27	28
29	30					

By the time she was six, she knew that she wanted to be a writer. At eleven, her first story was published in the *Washington Post.* She was paid $2.00. At fifteen, she entered her story "The Reincarnation of Miss Hetty" in a *McCall's* magazine contest, which she won.

Marjorie Kinnan Rawlings
(August 8, 1896 — December 14, 1953)

In 1928, Marjorie Rawlings and her husband bought a seventy-two acre orange grove at Cross Creek, Florida. In the sparsely populated back country of northern Florida, she found the setting for most of her successful fiction. Her first novel, *South Moon Under,* was a Book-of-the-Month Club selection. Her reputation was made, though, with the publication of *The Yearling* in 1938. She won the Pulitzer Prize, the movie rights were sold, and the novel has become a classic.

The Yearling, one year in the life of the Baxter family living in the Florida river country, tells the story of young Jody Baxter and Flagg, the fawn. "The book smells of sweat and wind, rain and parching corn, wood fires and herb brews, courage and clean despair," wrote critic Frances Woodward.

The idea for the book was suggested by her editor, the legendary Maxwell Perkins. But it is Rawlings' poetic writing and her realistic philosophy that endure. After the death of the deer, Jody's father teaches his son that "life knocks a man down and he gits up and it knocks him down agin."

Marjorie Rawlings found people difficult, but she was remarkably attuned to nature, to the weather, and to the cycle of the seasons. There's something haunting and timeless in her best writing. "Sorrow was like the wind. It came in gusts, shaking the woman. She braced herself," she wrote in *South Moon Under.* Or this passage from *The Sojourner,* published the year that she died: "They were all too tightly bound together, men and women, creatures wild and tame, flowers, fruits and leaves, to ask that any one be spared. As long as the whole continued, the earth could go about its business."

She also had a sharp eye for humor in the Florida backwoods. In her short story "Benny and the Bird Dogs," Benny buys seven dogs from money he had made selling gopher holes to Yankees. The dogs sit on the front porch in seven rocking chairs, and Benny's wife complains that "I don't close my eyes for the fuss."

As a writer, she found her sense of place in Florida. Fittingly, Marjorie Rawlings' final resting place is there, in a peaceful cemetery in Island Grove.

The Great War

When the guns of August 1914 first began to sound, poet Rubert Brooke wrote, "Now, God be thanked Who has matched us with His hour . . ." Neither Brooke, who would perish in the Great War the following year, nor the men and women of his gilded, optimistic age could have anticipated the carnage that was to follow. In four terrible years World War I gave birth to T.S. Eliot's "wasteland" and Joseph Roth's "flight without end." "History," observed philosopher José Ortega y Gasset in 1914, "is trembling to its very roots, its flanks are torn apart convulsively, because a new reality is about to be born."

Among those to bear the scars of this new reality was a generation of writers. To a few of these, such as the satirist Hector Hugh Munro ("Saki"), the war was a great adventure. "It seems almost too good to be true that I am going to take an active part in a big European war," Munro told his sister shortly before going to France in 1915. He died there a year later.

Enthusiasm like Munro's was rare. "From the soldier's point of view the real curse of this war is stagnation," said Australian writer Adrian Consett Stephen, who was killed in action near Ypres in 1918. Likewise appalled by the war's banality was British poet Wilfred Owen, who asked, "What passing-bells for these who die as cattle? / Only the monstrous anger of the guns."

Owen died in combat just seven days before the Armistice, one of the last of the Great War's ten- to thirteen-million victims, many of whom were writers. Among them was the German poet Gerrit Engelke, who pleaded, "But spare me, Death; / I am still in the first flush of youth." The Czech writer Frantisek Gellner, another of the war's victims, put it more plainly: "I want to get drunk again, I want to get drunk again on champagne!!!"

Those who survived the war endured their own brand of hell. "I didn't know that a war has no end for those who fought it," said the Italian writer Curzio Malaparte. In America, writers Ernest Hemingway, e.e. cummings, and John Dos Passos—all of whom served as ambulance drivers in the war—transformed the bitter yield of their battle experience into such novels as *A Farewell to Arms*, *The Great Room*, and *U.S.A.*

In England, in a eulogy for her friend Rupert Brookes, poet Frances Cornford spoke for, and about, a generation:

> *A young Apollo, golden-haired,*
> *Stands dreaming on the verge of strife,*
> *Magnificently unprepared*
> *For the long littleness of life.*

Sunday
11
Louise Bogan, b. 1897

Monday
12

Edith Hamilton, b. 1867

Tuesday
13

● *Wednesday*
14

Thursday
15

Edna Ferber, b. 1855
Sir Walter Scott, b. 1771
Thomas De Quincey, b. 1785

Friday
16

Saturday
17

July						
S	M	T	W	T	F	S
	1	2	3	4	5	6
7	8	9	10	11	12	13
14	15	16	17	18	19	20
21	22	23	24	25	26	27
28	29	30	31			

August
1996

September						
S	M	T	W	T	F	S
1	2	3	4	5	6	7
8	9	10	11	12	13	14
15	16	17	18	19	20	21
22	23	24	25	26	27	28
29	30					

Sunday
18

Monday
19

Ogden Nash, b. 1902

Tuesday
20

Wednesday ◑
21

Thursday
22

Dorothy Parker, b. 1893

Friday
23

Edgar Lee Masters, b. 1868

Saturday
24
Jorge Luis Borges, b. 1899

July						
S	M	T	W	T	F	S
	1	2	3	4	5	6
7	8	9	10	11	12	13
14	15	16	17	18	19	20
21	22	23	24	25	26	27
28	29	30	31			

August
1996

September						
S	M	T	W	T	F	S
1	2	3	4	5	6	7
8	9	10	11	12	13	14
15	16	17	18	19	20	21
22	23	24	25	26	27	28
29	30					

He was the bane of biographers—a genuinely happy man who married a lovely woman, had two fine daughters, worked hard, and died with "no fuss, no trouble . . . as gently as he had lived." After researching his life, one potential biographer moaned, "There's no money in this stuff—it reads like something for *Reader's Digest*."

In compiling a collection of her father's correspondence, titled *Loving Letters from Ogden Nash*, Linell Nash Smith has proven that the life of a fulfilled, contented person can still be fascinating. Nash's letters reveal an ardent, charming, always witty man. To his wife he wrote: "When you storm I feel like this (A single sad parenthesis . . ." In another letter, he said: "I know that a little verse is a versicle, but I don't know if a little phrase is a phrasicle."

During the turbulent, tragic 1960s, though, Nash wondered if his verses were relevant. "In a world gone mad," he told his daughter, "humor may have been the first casualty of war." Actually, Nash used humor as "a shield, a weapon, a survival kit" against the exigencies of life.

Ogden Nash
(August 19, 1902 — May 19, 1971)

Early on, Nash decided that he would "rather be a great bad poet than a bad good poet." He dropped out of Harvard, taught French for awhile, wrote advertising copy, and finally landed a job as an associate editor at Doubleday. A few years later, Harold Ross at *The New Yorker* lured him away to serve as Managing Editor, a job that lasted just three months, although his verse continued to appear in the magazine. For six years he worked as an editor at Farrar and Rinehart, before resigning to write full time. All in all, he wrote fourteen volumes of poetry, co-authored the hit Broadway play *One Touch of Venus*, and in a lifetime of work "altered the sensibility of his time."

Nash worked at home in his library or sitting room, composing his poems on yellow legal pads, on scratch paper by the telephone, on the backs of envelopes, whatever happened to be lying around. If not a great poet, he was certainly one of the most quotable. In *Reflections on Ice-Breaking*, he wrote:

> *Candy*
> *Is dandy*
> *But liquor*
> *Is quicker.*

As a poet, Nash suffered two disadvantages, quipped Clifton Fadiman. "He is a humorist and he is easy to understand."

Maurice Maeterlinck
(August 29, 1862 — May 6, 1949)

A man of contradictions, Maurice Maeterlinck loved fine wines and good food, boxing, bees, women, and the mysteries of language. He welcomed friends into his house but shied away from crowds, and throughout his life he sought places of refuge where he could escape from human society. At one point he rented a fourteenth-century Benedictine Abbey in Normandy. There, his wife Georgette wore nun's mantles while the ever-practical Maeterlinck used roller skates to get from one vast hallway to the next.

He was obsessed with the mystical side of life, perhaps as a result of the "seven years of tyranny" he endured as a young man at a Jesuit college in his native Ghent. Subjected to daily sermons about sin and damnation, forced to eat from utensils that "were so greasy they slid through one's fingers like eels," and above all exposed to the bigotry of the institution's Fathers, Maeterlinck emerged from the place a confirmed agnostic. "There is only one crime which cannot be forgiven," he later said, "that of having poisoned the joys and destroyed the smile of a child."

He went on to study law at his father's insistence, but he detested every minute of it. By nature Maeterlinck was a writer. He composed his first plays in childhood. After receiving his law degree he moved to Paris, ostensibly to further his legal career. In fact, he spent much of his time in cafés, listening to Symbolist poets read from their work. At his own expense Maeterlinck published his first volume of poetry as well as his first play in 1889. At home in Belgium, his mother secretly juggled the family's budget in order to help offset her son's publication costs.

In 1891, with the premiere of his play *The Intruder*, Maeterlinck at last gained notice as a writer. The play, a Symbolist tale about death's visitation upon a family, struck critic Octave Mirbeau as "a masterpiece." In his review of the work, Mirbeau wondered aloud if Maeterlinck's play was not "superior in beauty to what is most beautiful in Shakespeare?" The playwright was dumbstruck. "You were wrong in considering me a great poet," he told Mirbeau. "I am merely a groping child."

In *The Intruder*, as in all the poems, plays, essays and stories he produced in his lifetime, Maeterlinck endeavored to fulfill what he believed was the writer's primary task, "to receive and impart profound truths." To this sacred calling the reclusive Belgian author consecrated his life.

Sunday
25

Monday
26

Summer Bank Holiday (UK)

Tuesday
27

Theodore Dreiser, b. 1871

○ *Wednesday*
28

Johann Wolfgang Goethe, b. 1749

Thursday
29

Maurice Maeterlinck, b. 1862

Friday
30

Mary Wollstonecraft Shelley, b. 1797

Saturday
31
William Saroyan, b. 1908

July						
S	M	T	W	T	F	S
	1	2	3	4	5	6
7	8	9	10	11	12	13
14	15	16	17	18	19	20
21	22	23	24	25	26	27
28	29	30	31			

August
1996

September						
S	M	T	W	T	F	S
1	2	3	4	5	6	7
8	9	10	11	12	13	14
15	16	17	18	19	20	21
22	23	24	25	26	27	28
29	30					

Sunday
1
Edgar Rice Burroughs, b. 1875

Monday
2

Labor Day

Tuesday
3

Sarah Orne Jewett, b. 1849
Treaty of Paris ends Revolutionary War, 1783

Wednesday ◑
4

Richard Wright, b. 1908
Antonin Artaud, b. 1896

Thursday
5

Friday
6

Saturday
7

August						
S	M	T	W	T	F	S
					1	2	3
4	5	6	7	8	9	10
11	12	13	14	15	16	17
18	19	20	21	22	23	24
25	26	27	28	29	30	31

September
1996

October						
S	M	T	W	T	F	S
		1	2	3	4	5
6	7	8	9	10	11	12
13	14	15	16	17	18	19
20	21	22	23	24	25	26
27	28	29	30	31		

Writing a fantastic story about Mars starring a super-hero named John Carter seemed a "foolish thing" for a thirty-five-year-old man to be doing, but he had a wife and babies to support, and his latest business venture (selling pencil sharpeners on commission) wasn't going well. He was ashamed of his writing and had finished half the story before he told his wife what he was doing. Titled *Under the Moons of Mars*, the story sold for $400. He was on his way.

Later, Ed Burroughs would say that his life hadn't been exciting. "I am one of those fellows who has few adventures and always gets to the fire after it is out." He grew up on the west side of Chicago, briefly attended Phillips Academy in Andover, Massachusetts, was sent to military school, served with the 7th U.S. Cavalry in the Arizona Territory, and failed at

Edgar Rice Burroughs
(September 1, 1875 — March 19, 1950)

so many jobs that he lost count. The soldiers, cowboys, and Indians whom he knew would have provided ample material for a writer interested in realism, but Burroughs had no use for the everyday world. He wanted to escape into the high adventure of his imagination.

Since he wasn't "literary and afflicted with temperament" he didn't mind that his children climbed all over him as he worked. He wrote from 7:30 a.m. till noon, typing his stories with two fingers. He imagined the plot as he went along, polishing his sentences in his head before writing them down, and he averaged ten to twelve double-spaced pages a day. He told aspiring writers to "forget style . . . Write in the way that interests you most, tell the stories that you are interested in and if you cannot succeed in this way it is because nature never intended you for a writer."

Burroughs preferred his science fiction stories, but readers loved his tales about little Lord Greystoke who was abandoned in Africa, raised by apes, and became *Tarzan of the Apes, the Lord of the Jungle*. Writer Ray Bradbury read the Tarzan books as a boy. "We may have liked Verne and Wells and Kipling," Bradbury said, "but we loved, we adored, we went quite mad with Mr. Burroughs. We grew up into our intellectuality, of course, but our blood always remembered . . . Because of him we have printed the Moon."

Edgar Rice Burroughs died in bed one day after reading the comics. The man who created so many strange and fantastic worlds was an atheist. "If there is a hereafter," he had said, "I want to travel through space to visit the other planets."

Roald Dahl

(September 13, 1916 — November 23, 1990)

Roald Dahl did not intend to become a writer. He wanted, instead, to go to faraway places and to have adventures. And so at the age of twenty-one, when the Shell Oil Company offered him a position in East Africa, he leapt at the chance. "Lions!" he cried. "And elephants and giraffes and coconuts everywhere!"

While he was in Africa, World War II broke out and Dahl joined Britain's Royal Air Force. He was twenty-three years old. He became a pilot and nearly died in a crash landing in the Libyan desert in 1940. Later he fought the Germans in Greece, and still later he was sent to Washington, D.C., as a member of the British diplomatic corps. His duties included spying on the United States government, a job for which Dahl was especially well suited because of his independent spirit, his fondness for solitude, and his innate distrust of rules and regulations.

In Washington, Dahl met the celebrated British writer C.S. Forester, author of the Horatio Hornblower series. Forester hoped to write an article about Dahl's most exciting experience as a pilot. But Dahl volunteered to draft his own version of the story instead, and when he showed the result to Forester, the older writer exclaimed, "Your piece…is the work of a gifted writer." Forester submitted Dahl's story, untouched, to the *Saturday Evening Post*, who published it. In that instant Roald Dahl became a writer.

He spent the 1940s and early 1950s writing and publishing short stories for adults. For years Dahl wrote in a cold and cluttered brick hut in an apple orchard outside his home in England, where he lived with his wife, the actress Patricia Neal, and their children.

In 1960 he decided to "have a go at doing a children's book." Dahl had long been inventing bedtime stories for his children, and he now took one of those tales—about a gigantic peach— and turned it into a book called *James and the Giant Peach*. Thus began Roald Dahl's second career, as a children's book author.

In his books for children Dahl was able to recall and reinvent his own childhood—both the happiness of his family life in Wales and the misery of his years in English boarding schools, where monstrous teachers beat children until they bled and the only joy came from periodic visits to the Cadbury chocolate factory.

Dahl knew instinctively how to appeal to children, perhaps because at some level he never stopped being one. Asked to reveal his formula for success as a children's book author, he replied that it consisted of "conspiring with children against adults."

Sunday
8

Monday
9

Leo Tolstoy, b. 1828

Tuesday
10

Hilda Doolittle, (H.D.), b. 1886

Wednesday
11

D.H. Lawrence, b. 1885
O. Henry, b. 1862

● *Thursday*
12

Friday
13

Roald Dahl, b. 1916
Rosh Hoshanah begins at sunset

Saturday
14

August						
S	M	T	W	T	F	S
				1	2	3
4	5	6	7	8	9	10
11	12	13	14	15	16	17
18	19	20	21	22	23	24
25	26	27	28	29	30	31

September
1996

October						
S	M	T	W	T	F	S
		1	2	3	4	5
6	7	8	9	10	11	12
13	14	15	16	17	18	19
20	21	22	23	24	25	26
27	28	29	30	31		

Sunday
15
Agatha Christie, b. 1890

Monday
16

Tuesday
17

William Carlos Williams, b. 1883
Constitution Day

Wednesday
18

Samuel Johnson, b. 1709

Thursday
19

Friday
20

Stevie Smith, b. 1902
Upton Sinclair, b. 1879

Saturday
21

August						
S	M	T	W	T	F	S
				1	2	3
4	5	6	7	8	9	10
11	12	13	14	15	16	17
18	19	20	21	22	23	24
25	26	27	28	29	30	31

September
1996

October						
S	M	T	W	T	F	S
		1	2	3	4	5
6	7	8	9	10	11	12
13	14	15	16	17	18	19
20	21	22	23	24	25	26
27	28	29	30	31		

Ogden Nash rhymed the right questions.

"Who and what is Stevie Smith? Is she woman? Is she myth?"

In her poems, which she called "sound vehicles," Stevie Smith adopted different personae and spoke in various voices, often comic, sometimes contradictory and teasingly ambiguous, but always compelling.

Born in Hull, Yorkshire, two months premature, she was given the plain, decidedly unpoetic name of Margaret Florence Smith. Because of her precocious, domineering nature, her family nicknamed her Miss Baby. Her father ran away to sea when she was three, and Stevie grew up surrounded by adoring women. For three years during her childhood, Stevie was separated from her family and sent to live in a boarding house to recover from tubercular peritonitis.

Stevie Smith
(September 20, 1902 — March 7, 1971)

Perhaps this is why at eight years old, she contemplated suicide. Thinking of suicide cheered her up, she said later. "For if one can remove oneself at any time from the world, why particularly now?"

As a child she read voraciously—Greek and Roman mythology, Hans Christian Andersen, Grimm's Fairy Tales, Lewis Carroll. "Reading is an appetite which grows as it feeds, and if you give it weak and second-rate stuff it will never grow strong," she observed. She had a talent for drawing and an excellent memory.

When she wrote her first poem, her practical Aunt Madge told her it was "unnecessary." But poetry was necessary for her survival. "I want to get something out that is working away at me inside. I think pressure is the operative word here."

One critic observed that through her work, Smith explored "the cavities of pain...to find a way out of their horror and darkness." After two novels and a collection of poems, she was famous. Her work moved women particularly. "If you knew the letters I still get," Smith told a friend. "The ones from the women—all so hungry & worrying. Hungry for a nostrum, a Saviour, a Leader, anything but to face up to themselves & a suspension of belief."

In her poetry, Smith faced pain, despair, loss, loneliness, alienation, and cruelty, but she was aware "of the ticklish comic element in human suffering" and she delighted in wordplay, titling one of her poetry volumes *Not Waving But Drowning*.

Suicide was always an option, but Smith never chose to "remove herself from the world." She composed her last poem as she lay dying, writing, "Come death. Do not be slow."

Red Smith
(September 25, 1905 — January 15, 1982)

"There's nothing to writing," he said. "All you do is sit down at the typewriter and open a vein."

For over half a century, from 1927 to 1982, Red Smith sat down at his typewriter and wrote. He had the "two left feet of a nonathlete," but he became the nation's most honored sportswriter and won the 1976 Pulitzer Prize for Distinguished Commentary, marking the first time a sportswriter won that honor.

Called Red because of his flaming brick-colored hair and because he loathed Walter Wellesley, his real name, the 5'6", extremely nearsighted writer never stopped working at his craft. Writing well was difficult, and as he aged it didn't get any easier. "I've read about Flaubert rolling on the floor for three days, groping for the right word," he said. "I can't afford three days. I'll blow two deadlines if I do."

Every year he reread E. B. White's *Elements of Style*. His columns were accurate, spare, direct, and literate. His goal was to entertain his readers, he said, and "capture the grace and drama and beauty and humor" in sports. He delighted in inventing collective nouns: "a bibulation of sportswriters, a yammer of radio announcers, a guilt of umpires, an indigence of writers."

He crafted each sentence meticulously and bridled at editors tinkering with his prose. When he wrote that a fighter was "surrounded in a corner by his seconds" and his editor substituted the verb "circled," Smith argued that "you can't 'circle a corner'." His phrase "bitten into an apple and found half a worm" was mangled by an editor who cut "half" and ruined the joke.

He was born and raised in Green Bay, Wisconsin. His high school yearbook prophesied that he would someday be a journalist on the *New York Times*—a prediction which came true in 1971. After graduating from Notre Dame with a degree in journalism, Smith embarked on a career that would take him around the globe. Babe Ruth, Joe DiMaggio, Ring Lardner, Ernest Hemingway, Muhammad Ali, and Tom Seaver were his friends. Marc Connelly assigned Smith's columns to his playwriting classes at Yale. In 1982 Smith's columns appeared in 275 papers in the United States and in 225 newspapers in thirty foreign countries.

His last column, filed just a few days before he died at the age of seventy-four of congestive heart failure, was titled "Writing Less—and Better?"

"Dying is no big deal," he wrote. "The least of us will manage that. Living is the trick."

Sunday
22
Yom Kippur begins at sunset   Fall Equinox, 2:01 pm EDT

Monday
23

Tuesday
24

Frances Ellen Watkins Harper, b. 1825 [?]

Wednesday
25

Red Smith, b.1905
William Faulkner, b. 1897

○ Thursday
26

Friday
27

Grazia Deledda, b. 1871

Saturday
28

August						
S	M	T	W	T	F	S
				1	2	3
4	5	6	7	8	9	10
11	12	13	14	15	16	17
18	19	20	21	22	23	24
25	26	27	28	29	30	31

September
1996

October						
S	M	T	W	T	F	S
		1	2	3	4	5
6	7	8	9	10	11	12
13	14	15	16	17	18	19
20	21	22	23	24	25	26
27	28	29	30	31		

Sunday
29
Miguel De Cervantes Saavedra, b. 1547   Elizabeth Gaskell, b. 1810

Monday
30

Truman Capote, b. 1924

Tuesday
1

Wednesday
2

Wallace Stevens, b. 1879

Thursday
3

Thomas Wolfe, b. 1900

Friday
4

Edward Stratemeyer, b. 1862
Damon Runyon, b. 1884

Saturday
5

August						
S	M	T	W	T	F	S
					1	2	3
4	5	6	7	8	9	10
11	12	13	14	15	16	17
18	19	20	21	22	23	24
25	26	27	28	29	30	31

September/October
1996

October						
S	M	T	W	T	F	S
		1	2	3	4	5
6	7	8	9	10	11	12
13	14	15	16	17	18	19
20	21	22	23	24	25	26
27	28	29	30	31		

The Tom Swift Series, The Rover Boys, The Hardy Boys, Nancy Drew, The Bobbsey Twins are just a few of the creations of the prolific author Edward Stratemeyer. He wrote 150 books under his own name and published 700 books using some seventy pen names, and founded a publishing syndicate that had a monopoly on children's literature for decades.

Arthur M. Winfield, the pen name he chose for the *Rover Boys Series*, indicates his approach to the business of writing. Arthur for author, M. for millions of copies sold, and Winfield for literally winning the field. Which he did. A national survey in 1926 demonstrated that out of 36,000 children, ninety-eight percent preferred Stratemeyer's books.

Stratemeyer was born in Elizabeth, New Jersey, to German immigrant parents. He grew up reading the dime novels penned by Horatio Alger, Jr., and he

Edward Stratemeyer
(October 4, 1862 — May 10, 1930)

absorbed the Alger philosophy that pluck and hard work led to sure success. He married and had two daughters who joined his syndicate and continued his work after his death.

Stratemeyer and his publishing syndicate never allowed biographers or reporters access to his personal life. Of course, the revelation that a whole library of authors was the work of one man and a few ghostwriters would certainly damage sales. Stratemeyer was said to have begun his writing career at twenty-four. While working at his brother's tobacco store, he dashed off an 18,000 word serial on wrapping paper, sent it to a Philadelphia boy's weekly, who bought it for $75.00 and told him to send more. By the time he was thirty-five years old, he had written sixteen books and six series, plus he had been chosen to finish the uncompleted works of Horatio Alger.

Along with fast-paced action and gripping plots, his books are riddled with cliches and ethnic stereotypes. "The Indians are on the warpath and they mean business." The characters get themselves "in a pickle." The bad guys eventually "turn over a new leaf." Foreigners with funny accents and tycoons in top hats are not to be trusted.

An assembly line worker in the Stratemeyer factory, Leslie McFarlane, under the name Franklin W. Dixon, continued the *Hardy Boys Series* and received $150 for each book. An impossibly modest man, McFarlane recalled that in the 1940s, his son came into his workroom one day and noticed the row of Hardy Boys books. "Why do you keep these books, Dad?" he asked. "Did you read them when you were a kid?" "Read them? I wrote them," replied McFarlane. "At least, I wrote the words."

Bruce Catton

(October 9, 1899 — August 28, 1978)

The most prominent individuals in Bruce Catton's many books about the United States Civil War are his fellow Midwesterners: Abraham Lincoln, William T. Sherman, and Ulysses S. Grant, men who shared Catton's frontier roots and Midwestern predilection for plainness, honesty, and individuality.

Catton often talked of his childhood in the northern Michigan town of Benzonia, a community founded in the 1850s by a group of Congregationalists from Ohio. Religion, coupled with a nineteenth-century faith in progress, permeated his youth. "We felt that the eye of God was constantly upon us," he remembered. At one point Catton's curiosity about religion led him to recreate the Crucifixion using an old rag doll and some scraps of wood. It was not the last time he would endeavor to bring history to life.

For a time he toyed with the idea of becoming a famous violinist, but his meager musical talents soon deprived Catton of that dream. Then, one day, after his father remarked on the interesting lives that reporters seemed to lead, Catton resolved to become a journalist.

He wrote his first book, *The War Lords of Washington*, during World War II, while serving as information director for the War Production Board in Washington. His first trilogy on the Civil War followed in the early 1950s, and Catton's reputation as a first-rank Civil War writer was born. The trilogy's final volume, *A Stillness at Appomatox*, won both the National Book Award and the Pulitzer Prize for history in 1954. Catton went on to write some fifteen additional books, most of them about the Civil War.

What distinguished Bruce Catton from his fellow historians was his eye for the revealing human detail, his gift for narrative, and his insistence on telling the story of the Civil War from the perspective of the men and women who had fought in it.

As a boy in Benzonia, Catton grew up among the aging veterans of America's Civil War. Each Memorial Day he watched these bearded old men in blue uniforms carry armloads of lilacs and tiny American flags to their fellow veterans who lay buried in the town graveyard. As the years wore on, the veterans gradually died off. "One by one," Catton recalled, "the old men went up to that sun-swept hilltop to sleep beneath the lilacs, and as they departed we began to lose more than we knew we were losing." That the lives of these heroic men are not altogether lost is due, in part, to the monumental work of author Bruce Catton.

Sunday
6
Caroline Gordon, b. 1895

Monday
7

Tuesday
8

Wednesday
9

Bruce Catton, b. 1899

Thursday
10

Friday
11

● *Saturday*
12

September

S	M	T	W	T	F	S
1	2	3	4	5	6	7
8	9	10	11	12	13	14
15	16	17	18	19	20	21
22	23	24	25	26	27	28
29	30					

October
1996

November

S	M	T	W	T	F	S
					1	2
3	4	5	6	7	8	9
10	11	12	13	14	15	16
17	18	19	20	21	22	23
24	25	26	27	28	29	30

Sunday
13

Monday
14

Katherine Mansfield, b. 1888
e. e. cummings, b. 1894
Columbus Day Observed
Thanksgiving Day (Canada)

Tuesday
15

Virgil, b. 70 B.C.

Wednesday
16

Oscar Wilde, b. 1854
Eugene O'Neill, b. 1888
Noah Webster, b. 1758

Thursday
17

Friday
18

Saturday
19

September						
S	M	T	W	T	F	S
1	2	3	4	5	6	7
8	9	10	11	12	13	14
15	16	17	18	19	20	21
22	23	24	25	26	27	28
29	30					

October
1996

November						
S	M	T	W	T	F	S
					1	2
3	4	5	6	7	8	9
10	11	12	13	14	15	16
17	18	19	20	21	22	23
24	25	26	27	28	29	30

She was a master of the short story, and other writers envied her gifts. Particularly Virginia Woolf who said that her work was "the only writing I have ever been jealous of." She can write, damn her, said Rupert Brooke. How did she do it? Lady Ottoline believed that it was because she was never off-duty as a writer.

Chekhov was her primary influence, but when she saw Van Gogh's *Sunflowers* she learned "something about writing which was queer, a kind of freedom— or rather, a shaking free." She wanted to write simply, with "no fine effects—no bravura"— telling "the plain truth as only a liar can tell it."

She was born Katherine Mansfield Beauchamp in Wellington, New Zealand, the disappointing third daughter in a family of daughters, since, as usual, a boy was wanted. When she was eighteen years old, she

Katherine Mansfield
(October 14, 1888 — January 9, 1923)

lopped off her father's name and became Katherine Mansfield. She was a published author at nineteen, and she spurned the "insipid doctrine" which taught women that "love is the only thing in the world." Like a man, she wanted "power, wealth and freedom."

Still, she loved fashionable clothes and expensive perfumes, and she had numerous flirtations with both men and women. After a bizarre one-day first marriage (she married and left her husband on the same day), she wed John Middleton Murray, a British editor and critic. Her circle of friends included Virginia Woolf's Bloomsbury, D.H. Lawrence (he based Gudrun in *Women in Love* on Mansfield), Dorothy Brett, T. S. Eliot, James Joyce, and Bertrand Russell.

When she was just twenty-nine years old, a "spot" was discovered on her lungs. Friends turned away, covering their faces with handkerchiefs when she coughed, fearing to catch the consumption. When she looked in the mirror she was frightened by the girl "with burning eyes."

She spent her last days in an old monastery with the spiritualist George Ivanovich Gurdjieff who told her "not to think, not to write...Live in your body again." She would relax in the hayloft inhaling the warm breath of the cows and drinking fresh milk from the milkpail. One evening when her husband was visiting, she longed for music. Then, impetuously, as a girl might, she ran up the stairs to her room. The blood gushed from her mouth. I believe I'm going to die, she said. She was thirty-five years old.

Moss Hart
(October 24, 1904 — December 21, 1961)

He was born, he liked to say, on the wrong end of Fifth Avenue. Home was a crowded railroad flat in the Bronx, and he grew up with "the grim smell of actual want always at the end of my nose." While the other boys in the neighborhood played baseball and gutter hockey, young Moss Hart sat on the curb and watched, dreaming of Broadway, a fantasy place he knew about only from the pages of *Theatre* magazine. One summer night, he sat silently on the stoop of the local candy store. One of the boys asked him, "What's in those books you're always reading?"

"Stories," Hart said. "What kind?" somebody asked. For the next two hours, thirteen-year-old Moss told his audience the story of Theodore Dreiser's *Sister Carrie*. "They listened bug-eyed and breathless," he remembered. "Listening to a tale being told in the dark is one of the most ancient of man's entertainments."

With only a seventh grade education, Moss Hart would become one of the most successful playwrights in the American theatre. His first job in the theatre was office boy for producer Augustus Pitou, and his first official duty was to fetch a cup of coffee and some aspirin—a fitting opening scene for a life in the theatre, he decided.

He wrote his first play, *The Beloved Bandit*, when he was seventeen. On opening night, he was sick in the men's room, beginning a tradition that would last a lifetime. "I have been sick in the men's room every opening night of a play of mine in theatres all over the country." His first play flopped, but with collaborator George S. Kaufman, he wrote hit after hit— *Once in a Lifetime, Merrily We Roll Along, You Can't Take It With You* (which won the Pulitzer Prize) and *The Man Who Came to Dinner*. "Collaboration is an infinitely more pleasurable way of working than working alone," he said. On his own, he wrote *The Lady in the Dark*, a hit musical about psychoanalysis, and the comic *Light Up the Sky*, about a playwright's first Broadway show. *Act One*, his hilarious and moving autobiography, is one of the best books ever written about a life in the theatre.

Telling tales in the dark moved him out of Bronx poverty and into Manhattan. He married actress Kitty Carlisle and fathered two children. He was working on a new comedy when he died of a heart attack at fifty-seven.

Sunday
20
Arthur Rimbaud, b. 1854

Monday
21

Samuel Taylor Coleridge, b. 1772

Tuesday
22

Wednesday
23

Thursday
24

Moss Hart, b. 1904

Friday
25

○ *Saturday*
26

September						
S	M	T	W	T	F	S
1	2	3	4	5	6	7
8	9	10	11	12	13	14
15	16	17	18	19	20	21
22	23	24	25	26	27	28
29	30					

October
1996

November						
S	M	T	W	T	F	S
					1	2
3	4	5	6	7	8	9
10	11	12	13	14	15	16
17	18	19	20	21	22	23
24	25	26	27	28	29	30

Sunday
27
Daylight Saving Time ends   *Sylvia Plath, b. 1932   Dylan Thomas, b. 1914*

Monday
28

Evelyn Waugh, b. 1903

Tuesday
29

Jean Giraudoux, b. 1882

Wednesday
30

Ezra Pound, b. 1885

Thursday
31

John Keats, b. 1795
Halloween

Friday
1

Stephen Crane, b. 1871

Saturday
2

September						
S	M	T	W	T	F	S
1	2	3	4	5	6	7
8	9	10	11	12	13	14
15	16	17	18	19	20	21
22	23	24	25	26	27	28
29	30					

October/November
1996

November						
S	M	T	W	T	F	S
					1	2
3	4	5	6	7	8	9
10	11	12	13	14	15	16
17	18	19	20	21	22	23
24	25	26	27	28	29	30

Stephen Crane was fascinated all his life with acts of courage and the color red.

In her moving, powerful biography of Stephen Crane, Linda H. Davis relates an episode of personal courage in Crane's life. He had seen a prostitute falsely arrested for soliciting and had gone to court to testify on her behalf. Although Crane's reputation was damaged by his defense of the prostitute, and the New York Police Department harassed him whenever he visited the city, Crane never regretted his valorous act. It was the right thing to do. Plus the prostitute, he said, "was really handsome, you know, and she had . . . red hair—dark red."

In *The Red Badge of Courage* he wrote, "They were going to look at war, the red animal—war, the blood-swollen god." Crane researched his first novel, *Maggie: A Girl of the Streets,* in New York's Bowery. He knew

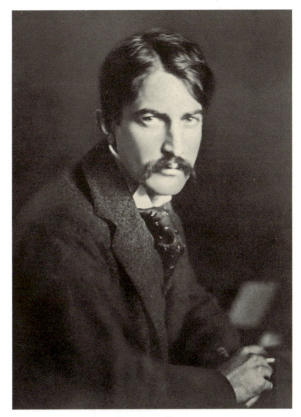

Stephen Crane
(November 1, 1871 — June 5, 1900)

first-hand what it was like to shiver in an unheated tenement and to stand for hours in a breadline. In contrast, *The Red Badge of Courage*, his novel of the Civil War, sprang entirely from his imagination. He had never been to war, never seen a battle.

One day as he walked along the beach with a friend, he threw sand into the air and offered this advice about writing: "Treat your notions like that. Forget what you think about it and tell how you feel about it."

With his impressionistic, ironic, metaphorical prose, Crane was ahead of the conventional writers of his time, and foreshadowed the work of Hemingway, Fitzgerald, and Faulkner. He influenced Willa Cather, who later described him as "thin to emaciation, his face was gaunt and unshaven, a thin dark moustache straggled on his upper lip . . ."

The lean, tawny-haired Crane *was* hungry, "hungry for color, form, action" as he traveled throughout the American West and Mexico, working as a journalist. He became a war correspondent in Europe, reported from Cuba, and devoted himself, John Berryman regretted, to "boring false wars, away from the passionate private real war in his mind." Still, Crane produced some of his greatest work after he'd seen war, including his novella, *The Monster,* and his short stories *"The Bride Comes to Yellow Sky"* and *"The Blue Hotel."*

In May of 1900, Crane was admitted to a tuberculosis sanitarium at Baadenweiler, in Germany's Black Forest. There, pale and weakened from hemorrhaging gouts of bright red blood, he died. He was twenty-eight years old.

Иванъ Сергѣевичъ
ТУРГЕНЕВЪ
род. 28-го Октября 1818 г.
ум. 22-го Августа 1883 г.

Ivan Sergeyevich Turgenev
(November 4, 1816 — September 3, 1883)

In all aspects of his life, Ivan Sergeyevich Turgenev was a misfit. He believed in change but was not a revolutionary. He was Russian to the core, but happy only in foreign countries. He devoted himself to the same woman for two decades, but knew she would never be his. "Pulled by two ideas, two countries, and two destinies, he suffered from constant inner conflict," writes Turgenev biographer Henri Troyat, "yet at the same time it gave him a kind of mournful satisfaction."

Dichotomy marked his life from birth. The son of an heiress, Turgenev grew up on a huge Russian estate with more than 5,000 peasant serfs. His childhood home had forty rooms and a staff that included gardeners, cooks, tailors, tutors, serf actors and even an orchestra. In charge of this splendor was Turgenev's tyrant mother, who whipped her young son "almost daily" for minor offenses and gave him, he later said, "an early loathing of slavery."

Taught by German and Swiss tutors, Turgenev learned his native tongue only by secretly reading Russian classics in his family's library. He learned Russian poetry from an old serf who recited verse to the boy as they took walks together on the Turgenev estate.

Young Ivan grew into a dreamlike teenager who loved reading, writing, and women. He drew one of his early stories, "First Love," from his discovery that a beautiful young woman with whom he had become infatuated was in fact his father's mistress. Throughout his life Turgenev's fiction would often reflect his desires and defeats in love.

His most famous work, *Fathers and Sons*, had less to do with love than with the conflict between generations. Turgenev based the novel's protagonist, the nihilist Bazarov, on a "young local doctor" whom he observed during a visit to the Isle of Wight. Although Tolstoy fell asleep while reading an early draft of the book, elsewhere in Russia *Fathers and Sons* profoundly shook its readers.

Turgenev spent most of his adult life doggedly pursuing Pauline Viardot, a French soprano married to an opera director. The novelist managed somehow to befriend the husband while courting the wife—with whom he seems to have had an illegitimate son. Turgenev spent his last years living on the fourth floor of the Viardots' Paris home, a revered member of the family. So that he could hear Pauline singing downstairs, he installed an acoustical tube.

On his deathbed in Paris in 1883, Turgenev uttered his last intelligible words to Pauline: "This is the queen of the fairies! How much good she has done!" At his request, the itinerant Russian was buried in St. Petersburg.

Sunday
3

Monday
4

Tuesday
5

Wednesday
6

Thursday
7

Friday
8

Saturday
9

October						
S	M	T	W	T	F	S
	1	2	3	4	5	
6	7	8	9	10	11	12
13	14	15	16	17	18	19
20	21	22	23	24	25	26
27	28	29	30	31		

November
1996

December						
S	M	T	W	T	F	S
1	2	3	4	5	6	7
8	9	10	11	12	13	14
15	16	17	18	19	20	21
22	23	24	25	26	27	28
29	30	31				

Sunday
10

Monday
11

Feodor Dostoevsky, b. 1821
Veterans' Day
Remembrance Day (Canada)

Tuesday
12

Sor Juana Inés de la Cruz, b. 1651

Wednesday
13

Saint Augustine, b. 354

Thursday
14

Friday
15

Marianne Moore, b. 1887

Saturday
16
George S. Kaufman, b. 1889

October						
S	M	T	W	T	F	S
		1	2	3	4	5
6	7	8	9	10	11	12
13	14	15	16	17	18	19
20	21	22	23	24	25	26
27	28	29	30	31		

November
1996

December						
S	M	T	W	T	F	S
1	2	3	4	5	6	7
8	9	10	11	12	13	14
15	16	17	18	19	20	21
22	23	24	25	26	27	28
29	30	31				

Eugene Ionesco "had a clown's face," observed John Lahr, "—a rutted forehead and a bald pate that gave him a memorably comical double-dome appearance." He was a revolutionary clown, armed with an arsenal of wit and a profound, absurdist vision.

His first play, *The Bald Soprano*, opened in Paris in May, 1950. Three people were in the audience. A bald soprano never appeared or was mentioned. The actors were deadly serious. It rained. The roof leaked. The play closed after six weeks. But with the production of *The Bald Soprano*, Ionesco placed a whoopee cushion under modern theatre. "I suddenly saw characters move on the stage who had come out of myself," said Ionesco. "I was frightened. By what right had I been able to do this?"

His characters, Mr. and Mrs. Smith, with their *non sequiturs*,

Eugene Ionesco
(November 26, 1912 — March 28, 1994)

cliché-ridden conversation, and pointless action, parodied the banality of domestic drama. Order and reason were rejected; anarchy reigned. Criticized for not conforming to either right or left wing orthodoxies, Ionesco wrote about the absurdity of the human condition. He saw himself in a writing tradition that began with Sophocles and continued through Shakespeare and Kleist.

When he was a boy, his first experience of the theatre was watching Punch and Judy shows in the Luxembourg Gardens in Paris. "I stayed there . . . enrapt for whole days . . . through the sight of these puppets that talked, moved, clubbed each other. It was the spectacle of the world itself . . ."

Ionesco was born in Rumania and educated at the University of Bucharest where he studied French. In his late twenties, he moved to Paris and began writing plays in French. In 1948 he wanted to learn English and set to work with a language text. He met the characters Mr. and Mrs. Smith in the text and he "learned not English but some astonishing truths—that, for example, there are seven days in the week, something I already knew." Ionesco's study of English burst forth into *The Bald Soprano*, a "tragedy of language."

Other plays followed—*The Lesson, The Chairs, Rhinoceros*. Where did they come from? "I have no ideas before I write a play," said Ionesco. "I have them when I have written the play or while I am not writing at all. I believe that artistic creation is spontaneous."

He told his diary: "I am writing, writing, writing. All my life I have been writing; I have never been able to do anything else."

Voltaire

(November 21, 1694 — May 30, 1778)

His adventures and misadventures rival those of his most famous creation, *Candide*. By rights, François-Marie Arouet—the man who later called himself "Voltaire"—should have enjoyed a comfortable life as the son of a prosperous Parisian tax collector. But young François flouted convention. As a schoolboy he cavorted with freethinkers and libertines. As a young man he offended his father by announcing that he wished to become a man of letters instead of a lawyer. In punishment, his father banished him to The Hague—where François promptly got into trouble with a young woman named Pimpette.

Back in Paris in 1716, François took to writing poems that some deemed offensive to the French Regent. The young author was arrested and spent eleven months in the Bastille. Released, he changed his name to Voltaire. And he went on writing.

With the triumphant premiere of his play *Oedipus* at the Comédie-Française in 1718, Voltaire was hailed as an equal to Racine and Corneille and awarded a royal pension. By rights his future should have been assured. But trouble, as always, followed. First he survived an attempt on his life, then a second stay in the Bastille, then three years in exile in England, where he complained, "I am born to run through all the misfortunes of life."

The ensuing years saw Voltaire fall in and out of favor with the court, argue with scientists and clergymen, engage in an incestuous affair with his niece, and gain election to the French Academy. All the while he managed to write—comedies, dramas, poems, treatises, letters, and novels. At his death Voltaire's complete works ran to seventy-two volumes. The most famous of these was the novel *Candide*, Voltaire's devastatingly satirical answer to the popular notion that "the World is the best of all possible worlds."

Candide's author lived to be eighty-three. Despite a "cadaverous face" and bad teeth, he managed to dance, write books, and entertain his friends right up to the end. Thanks to a lifetime of wise investment, Voltaire died a rich man. But he, more than most, knew how little money mattered. As the hero of his novel *Micromégas* instructs, there are in life but two true sources of happiness: love and thought.

Sunday
17

Monday
18

W. S. Gilbert, b. 1836

Tuesday
19

Wednesday
20

Thursday
21

Voltaire, b. 1694

Friday
22

George Eliot, b. 1819

Saturday
23

October						
S	M	T	W	T	F	S
		1	2	3	4	5
6	7	8	9	10	11	12
13	14	15	16	17	18	19
20	21	22	23	24	25	26
27	28	29	30	31		

November
1996

December						
S	M	T	W	T	F	S
1	2	3	4	5	6	7
8	9	10	11	12	13	14
15	16	17	18	19	20	21
22	23	24	25	26	27	28
29	30	31				

Sunday   ○
24

Monday
25

Lope de Vega, b. 1562

Tuesday
26

Eugene Ionesco, b. 1912

Wednesday
27

Thursday
28

Thanksgiving Day

Friday
29

C. S. Lewis, b. 1898
Louisa May Alcott, b. 1832

Saturday
30
Mark Twain, b. 1835   Lucy Maud Montgomery, b. 1874

October						
S	M	T	W	T	F	S
				1	2	3	4	5
6	7	8	9	10	11	12
13	14	15	16	17	18	19
20	21	22	23	24	25	26
27	28	29	30	31		

November
1996

December						
S	M	T	W	T	F	S
1	2	3	4	5	6	7
8	9	10	11	12	13	14
15	16	17	18	19	20	21
22	23	24	25	26	27	28
29	30	31				

As a child, he had lots of names—"Jacks, Jacko, Jack, Kricks" and sometimes "It." As an adult, he wore many faces—scholar, literary historian, children's author, Christian apologist, and romantic lover.

Who was Clive Staples Lewis? In his 1990 biography, A. N. Wilson reveals the real man behind his many masks. The catastrophe of Lewis's life, says Wilson, was the death of his mother when he was nine years old. He bottled up the grief he felt, and years later married Joy Davidson, "whose circumstances were exactly parallel to those of his own mother ... a woman dying of cancer who had two small sons."

The marriage of C. S. Lewis to the abrasive, foul-mouthed, young and attractive Joy Davidson was made into a television movie, a Broadway play called *Shadowlands*, and a

C. S. Lewis
(November 29, 1898 — November 22, 1963)

feature movie. After Joy's death, Lewis poured his sorrow into *A Grief Observed*. "No one ever told me that grief felt so like fear," he wrote. The book and its "burning truths" have helped thousands of readers cope with their own suffering.

Millions of others have stepped with Lewis into the magical wardrobe and discovered Narnia—*The Lion, the Witch, and the Wardrobe* and the other six books in *The Chronicles of Narnia*. Lewis saw the allegorical stories first as pictures in his mind—"of a Faun carrying an umbrella and parcels in a snowy wood"—and writing the tale helped him to "steal past a certain inhibition which had paralyzed much of my own religion in childhood."

Lewis was born in Belfast, Ireland, the second son of Albert and Flora Lewis. After the death of their mother, the brothers were packed off to boarding school in England. Lewis never got over the brutality he experienced there, calling the school a "concentration camp."

He escaped into literature. As a teenager he had no experience of love, but claimed that what he did have was better—"the experience of Sappho, of Euripides, of Catullus, of Shakespeare, of . . .—anyone else I have read." He studied at Oxford, lectured there, and later left to become Professor of medieval and Renaissance Literature at Cambridge, a post he held until shortly before his death. When not puffing on his pipe, he smoked three packs of cigarettes a day, and he had a bullying bad temper. "You could always tell when he was going to start an argument," said a teaching colleague. "He would push forward his thick lower lip."

He died of heart failure on the same day that John F. Kennedy was assassinated. The phrase (taken from *King Lear*) "Men must endure their going hence" is carved on his headstone.

Rainer Maria Rilke
(December 4, 1875 — December 29, 1926)

In an otherwise peripatetic life, one thing was steadfast: Rainer Maria Rilke's devotion to his art. He once advised a young poet to "ask yourself in the stillest hour of your night: must I write?" If yes, "then build your life according to this necessity. Your life even into its most indifferent and slightest hour must be a sign of this urge and a testimony to it."

A character in one of Rilke's short stories suggests that "art is childhood," that in creating art one is making a new world without destroying the old. Rilke himself insisted that childhood— "that precious, kingly possession, that treasure-house of memories"—was a rich resource for any writer.

His own childhood was mercilessly short. His parents divorced when he was still a boy, and at the age of ten he was sent to a military academy in Austria. He later referred to the "evil and frightened half-decade" he spent in military school.

As an adolescent Rilke displayed what his Uncle Jaroslav called an "overheated" imagination. Jaroslav had hoped his nephew would take over the family law firm. But Rilke chose instead to write stories and poems. He published his first book, *Life and Songs*, in 1894 with a friend's financial help. In 1899, in a burst of white-heat inspiration, he composed *The Lay of Love and Death of Cornet Christoph Rilke* in a single night. The book, a collection of prose poems recounting the last days of a noble Saxon officer, established Rilke's name. After writing it the poet sent the work to his wife, sculptor Clara Westhoff, urging her to "read it, on one of your beautiful evenings, in your white dress."

Rilke spent much of his life wandering from one place to another in search of sites and circumstances conducive to work. Most famously, in 1912, a prolonged stay in the castle of Duino, near Trieste, inspired Rilke to write the *Duino Elegies*, a collection the poet considered his finest.

Rilke believed that poetic creation could spring from the most commonplace of events— a woman sewing by the window, the sound of a bird, the glance of a passerby. "Confederates of inspiration," he called such occasions. "If your daily life seems poor, do not blame it," he told an aspiring writer. "Blame yourself, tell yourself that you are not poet enough to call forth its riches."

Sunday
1

Monday
2

◑ Tuesday
3

Wednesday
4

Rainer Maria Rilke, b. 1875

Thursday
5

Chanukkah begins at sunset

Friday
6

Susannah Moodie, b. 1803

Saturday
7

Willa Cather, b. 1873   Pearl Harbor Day

November						
S	M	T	W	T	F	S
					1	2
3	4	5	6	7	8	9
10	11	12	13	14	15	16
17	18	19	20	21	22	23
24	25	26	27	28	29	30

December
1996

January 1997						
S	M	T	W	T	F	S
			1	2	3	4
5	6	7	8	9	10	11
12	13	14	15	16	17	18
19	20	21	22	23	24	25
26	27	28	29	30	31	

Sunday
8

Monday
9

Tuesday ●
10

Emily Dickinson, b. 1830

Wednesday
11

Thursday
12

Gustave Flaubert, b. 1821

Friday
13

Saturday
14
Shirley Jackson, b. 1919

November						
S	M	T	W	T	F	S
					1	2
3	4	5	6	7	8	9
10	11	12	13	14	15	16
17	18	19	20	21	22	23
24	25	26	27	28	29	30

December
1996

January 1997						
S	M	T	W	T	F	S
			1	2	3	4
5	6	7	8	9	10	11
12	13	14	15	16	17	18
19	20	21	22	23	24	25
26	27	28	29	30	31	

One of literature's most exacting practitioners, Gustave Flaubert spent most of his fifty-eight years sitting at the same desk, in the same room, in the same house, sculpting sentences. "I am like a row of milk pans," he confessed. "If you want the cream to form, you have to leave them exactly where they are." He rarely finished more than a paragraph or two a day. In his lifetime Flaubert published only five novels. A sixth appeared posthumously.

He sacrificed his life to his art. Monklike, he renounced children and marriage, which he called "an apostasy." Although he cavorted with prostitutes throughout his life, he was true to just one woman, his dour, hypochondriac, widowed mother, with whom he lived until her death in 1872, eight years before his own.

His only known liaison was with the poet Louise Colet, a tempestuous beauty from

Gustave Flaubert
(December 12, 1821 — May 8, 1880)

Provence. The two corresponded throughout the writing of Flaubert's masterpiece, *Madame Bovary*, whose protagonist the author drew, in part, from his knowledge of Colet. The book tormented Flaubert from start to end. "Now I foresee difficulties of style, and they terrify me," he told Colet in 1851, as he began drafting the novel. Three years later he complained, "As for finishing Bovary, I have already set myself so many dates, and been mistaken so often, that I refuse not only to speak of it but to think of it."

He completed the novel in 1855, and it was published serially the following year. The unsparing story of an adulterous wife in provincial France, *Madame Bovary* shocked most readers. "What?" cried one. "Such women exist?" The French government issued an indictment against the book on the grounds of "outrage to public morals and religion." Meanwhile, poet Charles Baudelaire praised its author for his astonishing portrait of female hysteria.

Despite such attention, Flaubert achieved only intermittent success with this and the other novels he published during his career. His genius, as critic Francis Steegmuller notes, "was even then understood as a phenomenon to be fully defined in a later age."

Death came quickly and unexpectedly to this least sentimental of writers. While taking a bath one night on the eve of a trip to Paris, Flaubert felt suddenly ill and sent his maid to fetch a doctor. "It's a good thing it's happening today," he said. "It would have been a nuisance tomorrow, on the train." These were his last coherent words. By the time the doctor arrived, Flaubert was dead.

Jean Genet
(December 19, 1910 — April 15, 1986)

The scene is a prison. A man arrested for stealing books is mistakenly forced to wear the uniform of a condemned prisoner. He writes a poem titled "The Man Condemned to Death." When he reads his poem aloud, the other prisoners laugh. "Poetry like that I squeeze out every morning," jibes one. The man doesn't care. He writes, he says, "for the drunkenness, the ecstasy, and to cut ever more deeply the links that still attached me to a world that rejected me and that I rejected in turn."

His life was epic theatre, and Jean Genet was a master of transformation. The irony, of course, is that the world came to embrace this thief, prostitute, con man, playwright, novelist, and poet. Simone de Beauvoir called him "a thug of genius." Sartre ironically christened him Saint Genet. An "autodidact of the jails," said one critic. The French cultural minister described him as a "black sun that enlightened the seamy side of things." After reading *Our Lady of the Flowers*, his discoverer and champion, Cocteau said, "To burn it would be too simple. It burns me . . . it's miraculous."

The miracle was that Jean Genet was able to write at all. Abandoned by his mother (he never knew his father), he was raised by peasants in a remote French village. In his monumental biography of Genet, Edmund White observes that as a child, Genet's favorite place to daydream was the outhouse. It "was the forcing shed of his imagination—a drowsy, shadowy place where he could inhale his own smells, those proofs of an inner corruption that later in prison he would greedily cup to his nose to inhale, as though he were an oracle posed above and inspired by the fumes of his body."

He languished for years in prison and wandered "from slum to slum" in Spain. Self-taught in the bitter school of the streets and from the books he devoured, Genet spun the dross of his experience into the gold of art. "He longed to write a play worthy of being performed in the theatre at Epidaurus," writes Edmund White. In addition to his five novels and other works, Genet wrote three extraordinary, incendiary plays (*The Balcony, The Blacks, The Screens*) that have indeed joined the Greek classics in the international repertory.

He moved among the rich and famous, but Genet rejected all the trappings of celebrity. One suitcase held all of his material possessions. He never owned a home. When his death came of throat cancer in a Paris hotel room, his burlap-wrapped coffin marked "immigrant worker" was flown to Morocco for burial in a run-down Spanish cemetery.

Sunday
15
Maxwell Anderson, b. 1888

Monday
16

Jane Austen, b. 1775
Noel Coward, b. 1899

 ## Tuesday
17

Wednesday
18

H.H. Munro (Saki), b. 1870

Thursday
19

Jean Genet, b. 1910

Friday
20

Saturday
21
Winter Solstice , 9:07 am EST

November						
S	M	T	W	T	F	S
					1	2
3	4	5	6	7	8	9
10	11	12	13	14	15	16
17	18	19	20	21	22	23
24	25	26	27	28	29	30

December
1996

January 1997						
S	M	T	W	T	F	S
			1	2	3	4
5	6	7	8	9	10	11
12	13	14	15	16	17	18
19	20	21	22	23	24	25
26	27	28	29	30	31	

Sunday
22

Monday
23

Giuseppe di Lampedusa, b. 1896

Tuesday ○
24

Juan Ramón Jiménez, b. 1881
Matthew Arnold, b. 1822

Wednesday
25

Christmas Day

Thursday
26

Jean Toomer, b. 1894
Boxing Day (Canada, UK)

Friday
27

Saturday
28

	November					
S	M	T	W	T	F	S
					1	2
3	4	5	6	7	8	9
10	11	12	13	14	15	16
17	18	19	20	21	22	23
24	25	26	27	28	29	30

December
1996

	January 1997					
S	M	T	W	T	F	S
			1	2	3	4
5	6	7	8	9	10	11
12	13	14	15	16	17	18
19	20	21	22	23	24	25
26	27	28	29	30	31	

A moody, enigmatic man, poet Juan Ramón Jiménez so needed peace and solitude in order to write that he lined his office walls with cork. He regularly shut himself away from visitors so that he could work. Once, to friends' astonishment, he walked from one part of his house to another while hiding behind a folding screen so as not to be seen by guests.

He was bewitchingly handsome. His long, finely chiselled face and domed brow might have been painted by El Greco. Women found him irresistible. But he was fundamentally a loner who suffered dire fears of death throughout his life, and was several times hospitalized for depression. He took as an early motto this line from Thomas à Kempis's *The Imitation of Christ*: "Show not thy heart to every man."

Juan Ramón Jiménez
(December 24, 1881 — May 29, 1958)

During his childhood in southern Spain, Jiménez roamed the countryside alone on his colt and spent long hours viewing the world through a kaleidoscope. In school he filled the margins of his textbooks with drawings. He dreamt first of being an artist, but in the end he chose words instead of paints as his medium and he became a poet. At age eighteen he published his first two books, *Violet Souls* and *Water Lilies*. The volumes were printed respectively in violet and green ink; their content was no less trite. Jiménez later turned his back on these florid works and destroyed all remaining copies of the books.

In 1916 his early, romantic style gave way to a concise, hermetic verse which Jiménez christened "naked poetry." He achieved the epitome of such poetry—and the pinnacle of his literary career—in the collections *Eternities* (1918), *Stone and Sky* (1919), *Poetry* (1923) and *Beauty* (1923), works in which Jiménez explored the role of poetry and expressed his longing to create a body of work as pure as the sky itself on a starry night.

At the start of the Spanish Civil War in 1936, Jiménez went into exile with his beloved wife, Zenobia. They spent the remainder of their lives in the United States and Puerto Rico. On October 25, 1956, Jiménez received the Nobel Prize for literature. Three days later Zenobia died from cancer. Disconsolate, Jiménez gave up writing altogether and spent the last months of his life staring at his wife's photographs and waiting for death. It came at last—the phantom that had once so terrified him—on May 29, 1958, at five o'clock in the morning.

The Reviewer's Art

Truman Capote put it bluntly. "I'll give you fifty dollars," he said, "if you produce a writer who can honestly say he was ever helped by the prissy carpings and condescensions of reviewers." Countless writers would agree.

The art of reviewing dates back at least to Aristophanes, who took pleasure in publicly trouncing his fellow authors' works by mocking them in his plays. He was kinder than some of his successors, whose caustic attacks have sometimes threatened to derail promising literary careers. Herman Melville was so devastated by several early reviews that he stopped writing for nearly forty years. William Inge was sufficiently upset by Robert Brustein's appraisal of his work that he telephoned the critic and wept over the receiver. Among other things, Brustein had called Inge "a fiddler with one string."

According to Saul Bellow, "Writers seldom wish other writers well." Perhaps he is right. Even so genteel an author as Elizabeth Barrett Browning once said publicly of Samuel Johnson, "[He] wrote the lives of the poets and left out the poets."

Both Coleridge and James Russell Lowell believed that those who took up the art of reviewing were people who had failed at other kinds of writing. As Lowell poetically phrased it, "Nature fits all her children with something to do, / He who would write and can't write, can surely review."

Not all reviews are bad, of course, nor do all writers object to criticism of their work. Mark Twain rejoiced when the Concord, Massachusetts, public library banned *Huckleberry Finn*. "That will sell 25,000 books for sure!" he crowed.

In fairness to reviewers, critics have their own public to consider as well, and bland praise, as Anthony Burgess has pointed out, is precisely that. Nonetheless, Burgess himself strove as a critic never to "stab anybody, for I know how life-denying it is to be stabbed. Writing a book is damned difficult work, and you ought to praise any book if you can."

For those who have been savaged by a review there is only one course of action, says sometime reviewer Anthony Brandt. "Avenge yourself. . . . Write well enough that someday your Reviewers will look like fools. Especially the famous ones, great writers themselves, who turned out to be terribly wrong about you."

Sunday
29

Monday
30

Tuesday
31

Wednesday
1

New Year's Day

Thursday
2

Friday
3

Saturday
4

December/January
1996/1997

Selected Sources

Abernethy, Cecil. *Mr. Pepys of Seething Lane*. New York: McGraw-Hill Book Company, Inc., 1957.

Alpers, Antony. *The Life of Katherine Mansfield*. New York: Penguin Books, 1982.

Ayer, A.J. *Voltaire*. London: Weidenfeld and Nicolson, 1986.

Baker, Carlos, ed. *Ernest Hemingway. Selected Letters 1917-1961*. New York: Charles Scribner's Sons, 1981.

Baker, Carlos. *Ernest Hemingway. A Life Story*. New York: Charles Scribner's Sons, 1969.

Benstock, Shari. *Women of the Left Bank*. Austin: University of Texas Press, 1986.

Berkow, Ira. *Red: The Life & Times of a Great American Writer*. Boston: G. K. Hall & Co., 1988.

Blinderman, Charles. "Charles Darwin." *Dictionary of Literary Biography*. Vol. 57. Detroit: Gale Research, Inc., 1987. Pages 50-70.

Boase, T.S.R. *Giorgio Vasari. The Man and the Book*. Princeton: Princeton University Press, 1971.

Brenan, Gerald. *St. John of the Cross. His Life and Poetry*. Cambridge: Cambridge University Press, 1973.

Brightman, Carol. *Writing Dangerously. Mary McCarthy and Her World*. New York: Clarkson Potter/Publishers, 1992.

Brosman, Catherine Savage. "Anatole France (Francois-Anatole Thibault)." *Dictionary of Literary Biography*. Vol. 123. Detroit: Gale Research, Inc., 1992. Pages 59-89.

Catton, Bruce. *Waiting for the Morning Train. An American Boyhood*. Garden City, New York: Doubleday, 1972.

Charlton, James ed. *Fighting Words*. Chapel Hill: Algonquin Books, 1994.

Childs, J. Rives. *Casanova*. New York: Paragon House Publishers, 1988.

Cross, Tim. *The Lost Voices of World War I. An International Anthology of Writers, Poets and Playwrights*. Iowa City: University of Iowa Press, 1988.

Drinkwater, John. *Pepys: His Life and Character*. Garden City, New York: Doubleday, 1934.

Esslin, Martin. *The Theatre of the Absurd*. Garden City, New York: Doubleday & Company, Inc. 1969.

Flanner, Janet. *Darlinghissima: Letters to a Friend*. Edited and with commentary by Natalia Danesi Murray. New York: Random House, 1985.

Franklin, H. Bruce. *Robert A. Heinlein: America as Science Fiction*. Oxford: Oxford University Press, 1980.

Geniesse, Jane. "Journey's End for a Legend. A Homage to the Late Dame Freya Stark, Intrepid Author of Travel Classics." *New York Times*. (September 26, 1993).

Gerstinger, Heinz. *Pedro Calderón de la Barca*. Translated by Diana Stone Peters. New York: Frederick Ungar Publishing Co., 1973.

Gill, Stephen. *William Wordsworth. A Life*. Oxford: Clarendon Press, 1989.

Gioia, Dana. "Longfellow in the Aftermath of Modernism." In Jay Parini, editor, and Brett C. Millier, associate editor. *The Columbia History of American Poetry*. New York: Columbia University Press, 1993. Pages 64-96.

Gray, Francine du Plessix. *Rage and Fire: A Life of Louise Colet. Pioneer Feminist, Literary Star, Flaubert's Muse*. New York: Simon and Schuster, 1994.

Hart, Moss. *Act One*. New York: Random House, 1959.

Ionesco, Eugene. *Present Past Past Present*. New York: Grove Press, 1971.

Izzard, Molly. *Freya Stark. A Biography*. London: Hodder & Stoughton, 1993.

Jean Cocteau and the French Scene. New York: Abbeville Press, 1984.

Kazin, Alfred. *A Writer's America. Landscape in Literature.* New York: Alfred A. Knopf, 1988.

Knapp, Bettina. *Maurice Maeterlinck.* Boston: Twayne Publishers, 1975.

Kudlinski, Kathleen V. *Rachel Carson. Pioneer of Ecology.* New York: Viking Kestrel, 1988.

Lahr, John. "Eugene Ionesco." *New Yorker.* April 11, 1994. Page 94.

Lewis, Allan. *Ionesco.* New York: Twayne Publishers, Inc. 1972.

Lodge, David. *The Art of Fiction. Illustrated from Classic and Modern Texts.* New York: Viking, 1992.

Mack, Sara. *Ovid.* New Haven: Yale University Press, 1988.

McCarthy, Mary. *How I Grew.* New York: Harcourt Brace Jovanovich, 1987.

Pepys, Samuel. *Passages From the Diary of Samuel Pepys.* Edited and with an introduction by Richard Le Gallienne. New York: The Modern Library, n.d.

Plimpton, George, ed. *The Writer's Chapbook: A Compendium of Fact, Opinion, Wit, and Advice from the 20th Century's Preeminent Writers.* New York: Viking, 1989.

Porges, Irwin. *Edgar Rice Burroughs. The Man Who Created Tarzan.* Provo, Utah: Brigham Young University Press, 1975.

Rilke, Rainer Maria. *Letters to a Young Poet.* Translated by M.D. Herter Norton. New York: Norton, 1934.

Rilke, Rainer Maria. *Where Silence Reigns. Selected Prose by Rainer Maria Rilke.* Translated by G. Craig Houston. Foreword by Denise Levertov. New York: New Directions, 1978.

Sandoz, Mari. *Crazy Horse.* A Bison Book.

Slusser, George Edgar. *Robert A. Heinlein Stranger in His Own Land.* San Bernadino, CA: The Borgo Press, 1977.

Smith, Linell Nash. *Loving Letters from Ogden Nash. A Family Album.* Boston: Little, Brown and Company, 1990.

Spalding, Frances. *Stevie Smith.* New York and London: W. W. Norton & Company, 1988.

Steegmuller, Francis. Foreword to *Flaubert-Sand: The Correspondence.* Translated from the French by Francis Steegmuller and Barbara Bray. Based on the edition by Alphonse Jacobs. With additional notes by Francis Steegmuller. New York: Alfred A. Knopf, 1993.

Stevenson, Lionel. *The Showman of Vanity Fair.* New York: Charles Scribner's Sons, 1947.

Thompson, Lawrence, and Winnick, R.H. *Robert Frost. A Biography.* New York: Holt, Rinehart and Winston, 1981.

Troyat, Henri. *Turgenev.* Translated from the French by Nancy Amphoux. New York: E. P. Dutton, 1988.

Wagenknecht, Edward. *Henry Wadsworth Longfellow. Portrait of an American Humanist.* New York: Oxford University Press, 1966.

West, Mark I. *Roald Dahl.* New York: Twayne Publishers, 1992.

White, Edmund. "The Celebration of Passion." *The New York Times Book Review.* (October 17, 1993).

White, Edmund. *Genet. A Biography.* New York: Alfred A. Knopf, 1993.

Wilson, A. N. *C. S. Lewis. A Biography.* New York: W. W. Norton & Company, 1990.

Wright, A. Colin. *Mikhail Bulgakov: Life and Interpretations.* Toronto: University of Toronto Press, 1978.

Young, Howard. "Juan Ramón Jiménez." *Dictionary of Literary Biography.* Vol. 134. Detroit: Gale Research, Inc., 1994. Pages 213-234.

Photo And Illustration Credits

About the Authors

The authors of "On Writers and Writing" are both biographers. Helen Sheehy is the author of *Margo: The Life and Theatre of Margo Jones*, published in 1989 by Southern Methodist University Press. Her biography of Eva Le Gallienne will be published by Alfred A. Knopf. A resident of Connecticut, Sheehy has written a theatre textbook, a number of articles and essays, and has taught theatre for over twenty years.

Leslie Stainton lives in Michigan and is at work on a biography of Federico Garcia Lorca for which she received a two-year Fulbright Research Grant. Her articles and essays have appeared in various newspapers and periodicals including the *New York Times,* the *Washington Post*, and *American Theatre* magazine.

Index

An alphabetical listing of writers or essay subjects and the week in which they appear: